Maths Facts

Developing Problem Solving Skills in the Daily Maths Lesson

Peter Clarke

Published by Collins Educational
An imprint of HarperCollins*Publishers* Ltd
77-85 Fulham Palace Road
Hammersmith
London
W6 8JB

www.CollinsEducation.com
On-line Support for Schools and Colleges

First published 2003

10 9 8 7 6 5 4 3 2 1

Acknowledgement
A special thanks to Brian Molyneaux. Without his help, and persistence on the Internet, this book would never have been written.

ISBN 0-00-715562-X

Publishing Manager: Melanie Hoffman
Project Editor: Ashley Lodge
Editor: Jean Rustean
Cover design by Chi Leung
Cover illustration by Tony Wilkins
Series design by Neil Adams
Illustrations by Tim Archbold of GCI, Juliet Breese, Roy Mitchell

Printed by Martins the Printers, Berwick on Tweed

Contents

Introduction

Maths Facts is a series of six books for Year 1 to Year 6. It uses topics taught in Science, Geography and History lessons to practise and consolidate the problem solving strand of the National Numeracy Strategy (NNS) *Framework for teaching mathematics from Reception to Year 6*. At the same time it develops other key mathematical concepts and skills from the numbers and the number system, calculations and measures, shape and space strands of the *Framework*.

This book contains 40 activities for a Year 6 class. Each activity consists of two parts. The first presents facts which cover the units and topics suggested in the Science, Geography and History programmes of study in the National Curriculum, and the relevant Qualifications and Curriculum Authority (QCA) schemes of work. The second part presents mathematical word problems which the children will answer by referring back to the relevant information they have been given.

Maths Facts not only develops children's mathematical ability but also reinforces the topics learnt in Science, Geography and History lessons and provides familiar and relevant contexts for the children to apply their problem solving skills.

The questions for each activity are differentiated into three levels: A, B and C. This caters for the needs of different ability groups within the class and enables each *Maths Facts* activity to be used at any time throughout the year.

Mathematical problem solving

Mathematical problem solving includes *applying mathematics* to the solution of problems arising from the environment and *reasoning* about questions that have arisen from the mathematics itself. Being able to use mathematics to analyse situations and solve real-life problems is a major reason for studying the subject. Frequent use of everyday scenarios will give meaning to the children's mathematical experiences. Children need to be able to apply the mathematics they have learned to real-life situations in their environment. They also need to be able to interpret and make meaning from their results. Teachers need to structure situations in which children investigate problems that are relevant to their daily lives and that relate to the mathematical knowledge, skills and understanding the children have most recently acquired.

Children also need to be made aware of the mathematics they are using to solve problems. Encouraging them to think about and discuss the strategies they use, and the knowledge and skills they have acquired, will assist children in developing a deeper understanding of mathematics. Discussions that arise out of mathematical problem solving can help children share experiences with each other and gain new knowledge, and will also assist them in developing their own mathematical vocabulary.

Problem solving skills

Maths Facts aims to develop in children the key skills required to tackle and solve mathematical problems. These include:

- reading and making sense of a problem
- recognising key words, relevant information and redundant information
- finding parts of a problem that can be tackled
- recognising the mathematics that can be used to help solve a problem
- deciding which number operation(s) to perform and in which order
- choosing an efficient way of calculating
- changing measurements to the same units before calculating
- getting into the habit of checking their own work to see whether the answer makes sense.

Strategies for solving mathematical problems

If children are to solve mathematical problems successfully they must be taught not only the mathematical concepts but also the strategies and procedures needed to apply these concepts. Children need to be taught to:

- look for a pattern or sequence
- experiment or act out a problem
- make a drawing or model
- make a list, table or chart
- write a number sentence
- see mathematical connections
- make and test a prediction
- make a generalisation
- establish a proof
- account for all known possibilities
- solve a simpler related problem
- work backwards.

An approach to solving mathematical problems

Children need to develop an effective and efficient method for solving mathematical problems. Page 7 provides them with a step-by-step approach to solving mathematical word problems. Photocopy and enlarge this page into a poster, and display it for all the class to see and follow during problem solving activities.

The seven steps to problem solving

Step 1 Read the problem carefully.

Step 2 What do you have to find?

Step 3 What facts are given?

Step 4 Which of the facts do you need?

Step 5 Make a plan.

Step 6 Carry out your plan to obtain your answer.

Step 7 Check your answer:
- Does it make sense?
- Put the answer back into the problem and check that it fits the information you were given.

Common pupil difficulties in problem solving

Sometimes children who are confident and capable at solving purely mathematical exercises, such as calculations, experience difficulties when it comes to solving problems. This may be due to difficulties with one or more of the following:

- reading the problem with understanding
- selecting the relevant information
- using the necessary mathematical expression
- making the required calculation correctly
- seeing relationships and using patterns
- using existing mathematical knowledge
- developing a systematic approach
- estimating the answer
- using trial-and-improvement techniques
- checking the answer
- seeing if the answer is reasonable
- recognising the connection between the answer achieved and the question asked
- being motivated
- perseverance
- confidence.

Suggestions for overcoming common pupil difficulties in problem solving

One or more of these strategies may help children who are experiencing difficulties with solving a problem.

- Present the problem orally.
- Discuss a possible approach with the children, asking appropriate questions.
- Revise any mathematical knowledge or skills needed to solve successfully the problem.
- Allow the children to work together, sharing their ideas for tackling a problem.
- Use smaller numbers.
- Use a pictorial approach if children are having difficulty with the abstract form of the problem.
- Use concrete apparatus to clarify the mathematics for the children.

- Allow the children to use appropriate resources such as a number line or hundred square to assist them with the mathematics.
- Allow the children to use a calculator.
- Use problems that are of relevance and interest to the children.

The teacher's role in problem solving lessons

- Give a choice where possible.
- Present the problem verbally, giving maximum visual support where appropriate.
- Enable children to own the problem.
- Encourage children to work together, sharing ideas for tackling a problem.
- Allow time and space for collaboration and consultation.
- Intervene, when asked, in such a way as to develop children's autonomy and independence.
- Encourage children to report the progress they are making.
- Work alongside children, setting an example yourself.
- Encourage the children to present their work to others.

The four types of word problem

All the activities in this book provide a balance between the four different types of word problem.

- The final quantity is unknown, e.g.
  - *Samantha has £1.35 and Jeanette has £1.65. How much money do they have altogether?*
  - *Matz baked 12 small cakes in each cake tin. He used two full tins. How many cakes did he bake?*
  - *Michael shared 20 grapes equally among himself and his four friends. How many did each person get?*
- The final quantity is known but not all the steps on the way, e.g.
  - *Berinda's mum baked 20 cookies. Berinda's friends came to play and ate some. How many were eaten if there were only 12 cookies left?*
  - *Sylvia needs 14 eggs. Each carton holds 6 eggs. How many cartons does she need?*
  - *Sam had 15 plants in a flower bed. He decided to throw out all the plants that were dying. He threw out 8 plants. How many plants did he keep?*

- Multi-step problems, e.g.
  - *There are 12 people on a bus. At the next stop 8 people get on and 5 get off. How many people are there on the bus now?*
  - *Steven's parents are taking Steven and his 2 sisters to the fun fair. Tickets cost £15.00 for adults and £12.50 for children. How much change do Steven's parents receive from £100?*
  - *I have enough wheels for 3 cars and there will be 2 over. How many wheels do I have?*
- Problems that involve comparisons between two or more sets, e.g.
  - *The number 59 bus has 16 people sitting downstairs and 27 people sitting upstairs. How many more people are sitting upstairs than are sitting downstairs?*
  - *I have 5 marbles, Louis has 3 and Brian has 12. Who has most? How many more does Brian have than Louis? How many more does Brian have than I do? How many more do I have than Louis?*

Maths Facts and the teaching–learning cycle

Assessment

- Guidance given on how to record pupil performance in AT1 – *Using and applying mathematics*.

Planning

- All activities provide practice and consolidation of the problem solving objectives in the NNS *Framework for teaching mathematics from Reception to Year 6*.
- Reference given to other relevant National Curriculum subjects, including National Curriculum programmes of study and QCA Primary schemes of work.
- Guidance given for planning a programme of work.

Teaching

- Consistent and easy-to-follow format for each activity.
- Guidance given on how to incorporate *Maths Facts* into the daily mathematics lesson.

Maths Facts and the daily mathematics lesson

The activities contained in *Maths Facts* are ideally suited to the daily mathematics lesson. Each activity is designed to be introduced to the whole class or group. A suggestion for a possible structure to a lesson using *Maths Facts* is given below.

- Oral work and mental calculation
  - Warm up the class by consolidating the knowledge and skills that will be used to solve the word problems.
  - Stimulate their involvement.
  - Emphasise the key vocabulary.
- Main teaching activity
  - Introduce the activity sheet to the children. Ensure that the children understand the picture and/or the vocabulary on the sheet.
  - Work through a couple of questions with the whole class, stressing possible problem solving strategies used.
  - Ask children to work in pairs on one or two of the problems.
  - Discuss these problems as a whole class.
- Pupil consolidation activities
  - Direct children's attention to the differentiated level(s) most appropriate to their needs.
  - Allow children to work individually or in pairs to solve the word problems.
  - Where needed, provide appropriate resources to assist children with the mathematics.
  - Monitor individuals, pairs or groups of children, offering support when and where necessary.
- Plenary
  - Plan an extended plenary.
  - Discuss one or two problems and possible solutions and strategies in depth with the whole class.
  - Give answers only to the remaining problems.

Curriculum information

The activities in this book provide children with an opportunity to practise and consolidate the following Year 6 problem solving objectives.

- Topic: *Making decisions*
  - Choose and use appropriate number operations to solve problems, and appropriate ways of calculating: mental, mental with jottings, written methods, calculator.
- Topic: *Reasoning and generalising about numbers or shapes*
  - Explain methods and reasoning, orally and in writing.
  - Solve mathematical problems or puzzles, recognise and explain patterns and relationships, generalise and predict. Suggest extensions asking 'What if…?'
  - Make and investigate a general statement about familiar numbers or shapes by finding examples that satisfy it.
  - Develop from explaining a generalised relationship in words to expressing it in a formula using letters as symbols.
- Topic: *Problems involving 'real life', money and measures*
  - Identify and use appropriate operations (including combinations of operations) to solve word problems involving numbers and quantities based on 'real life', money or measures (including time), using one or more steps, including converting pounds to foreign currency, or vice versa, and calculating percentages such as VAT. Explain methods and reasoning.

The National Numeracy Strategy curriculum coverage chart on page 13 shows which activity is matched to which NNS strand and topic.

The chart on pages 14–16 shows the theme for each *Maths Facts* activity and its link with the relevant National Curriculum programmes of study and QCA Primary schemes of work for Science, Geography and History.

National Numeracy Strategy curriculum coverage

Strand	Numbers and the number system			Calculations								Solving problems			Measures, shape and space		Handling data
Topic / Activity	Place value, ordering and rounding	Properties of numbers and number sequences	Fractions, decimals and percentages, ratio and proportion	Mental calculation Strategies (+ and −)	Paper and pencil procedures (+ and −)	Understanding multiplication and division	Rapid recall of multiplication and division facts	Mental calculation Strategies (× and ÷)	Paper and pencil procedures (× and ÷)	Using a calculator	Checking results of calculations	Making decisions	Reasoning and generalising about numbers or shapes	Problems involving: 'real life' (RL), money (MO), measures (ME)	Measures: Length (L), Mass (M), Capacity (C), Time (Ti), Temperature (Te), Area (A), Perimeter (P)	Shape and space	Organising and interpreting data
1	✔		✔	✔	✔	✔	✔	✔	✔	✔	✔	✔	✔	RL			
2	✔		✔	✔	✔	✔	✔	✔	✔	✔	✔	✔	✔	RL			
3			✔	✔	✔	✔	✔	✔	✔	✔	✔	✔	✔	RL			✔
4	✔		✔	✔	✔	✔	✔	✔	✔	✔	✔	✔	✔	RL			✔
5			✔	✔	✔	✔	✔	✔	✔	✔	✔	✔	✔	RL			✔
6			✔	✔	✔	✔	✔	✔	✔	✔	✔	✔	✔	RL			
7			✔	✔	✔	✔	✔	✔	✔	✔	✔	✔	✔	RL			
8			✔	✔	✔	✔	✔	✔	✔	✔	✔	✔	✔	RL			✔
9	✔		✔	✔	✔	✔	✔	✔	✔	✔	✔	✔	✔	RL			✔
10	✔		✔	✔	✔	✔	✔	✔	✔	✔	✔	✔	✔	RL			✔
11			✔	✔	✔	✔	✔	✔	✔	✔	✔	✔	✔	MO			✔
12			✔	✔	✔	✔	✔	✔	✔	✔	✔	✔	✔	MO			
13			✔	✔	✔	✔	✔	✔	✔	✔	✔	✔	✔	MO			✔
14			✔	✔	✔	✔	✔	✔	✔	✔	✔	✔	✔	MO			✔
15			✔	✔	✔	✔	✔	✔	✔	✔	✔	✔	✔	MO			
16			✔	✔	✔	✔	✔	✔	✔	✔	✔	✔	✔	MO			
17			✔	✔	✔	✔	✔	✔	✔	✔	✔	✔	✔	MO			✔
18	✔		✔	✔	✔	✔	✔	✔	✔	✔	✔	✔	✔	MO			✔
19			✔	✔	✔	✔	✔	✔	✔	✔	✔	✔	✔	MO			✔
20			✔	✔	✔	✔	✔	✔	✔	✔	✔	✔	✔	MO			✔
21	✔		✔	✔	✔	✔	✔	✔	✔	✔	✔	✔	✔	ME	Ti		✔
22	✔		✔	✔	✔	✔	✔	✔	✔	✔	✔	✔	✔	ME	M		✔
23	✔		✔	✔	✔	✔	✔	✔	✔	✔	✔	✔	✔	ME	L		✔
24			✔	✔	✔	✔	✔	✔	✔	✔	✔	✔	✔	ME	L		✔
25	✔		✔	✔	✔	✔	✔	✔	✔	✔	✔	✔	✔	ME	L/Te	✔	✔
26			✔	✔	✔	✔	✔	✔	✔	✔	✔	✔	✔	ME	M		✔
27			✔	✔	✔	✔	✔	✔	✔	✔	✔	✔	✔	ME	L/Ti		
28	✔		✔	✔	✔	✔	✔	✔	✔	✔	✔	✔	✔	ME	L		✔
29			✔	✔	✔	✔	✔	✔	✔	✔	✔	✔	✔	ME	L/A		✔
30	✔		✔	✔	✔	✔	✔	✔	✔	✔	✔	✔	✔	ME	M		✔
31			✔	✔	✔	✔	✔	✔	✔	✔	✔	✔	✔	RL/ME	M/A		
32	✔		✔	✔	✔	✔	✔	✔	✔	✔	✔	✔	✔	RL/ME	L/M/A		
33			✔	✔	✔	✔	✔	✔	✔	✔	✔	✔	✔	RL/ME	M/C/A		
34			✔	✔	✔	✔	✔	✔	✔	✔	✔	✔	✔	RL/ME	M/C/Ti		✔
35	✔		✔	✔	✔	✔	✔	✔	✔	✔	✔	✔	✔	RL/ME	M/C		✔
36	✔		✔	✔	✔	✔	✔	✔	✔	✔	✔	✔	✔	RL/MO/ME	L/A		
37	✔		✔	✔	✔	✔	✔	✔	✔	✔	✔	✔	✔	RL/MO/ME	L/A		
38	✔		✔	✔	✔	✔	✔	✔	✔	✔	✔	✔	✔	RL/MO/ME	L/M/Ti		✔
39	✔		✔	✔	✔	✔	✔	✔	✔	✔	✔	✔	✔	RL/MO/ME	M/C/Ti		✔
40	✔		✔	✔	✔	✔	✔	✔	✔	✔	✔	✔	✔	RL/MO/ME	M		✔

Links with National Curriculum programmes of study and QCA Primary schemes of work

Curriculum subject	Key Stage 2 National Curriculum programme of study	QCA Primary scheme of work	*Maths Facts* theme	Activity
Science	Sc2 Life processes and living things 1 Life processes 2 Humans and other animals 3 Green plants 4 Variation and classification 5 Living things and their environment Breadth of study: 1 / 2	6A Interdependence and adaptation	The Serengeti National Park	31
			Meerkats stand tall	32
	Sc2 Life processes and living things 1 Life processes 2 Humans and other animals 3 Green plants 5 Living things and their environment Breadth of study: 1 / 2	6B Micro-organisms	Deadly microbes	1
			Friendly microbes	11
	Sc3 Materials and their properties 1 Grouping and classifying materials 2 Changing materials 3 Separating mixtures of materials Breadth of study: 1 / 2	6C More about dissolving	Dissolving different foodstuffs	21
			Extracting salt by evaporation	33
	Sc3 Materials and their properties 1 Grouping and classifying materials 2 Changing materials 3 Separating mixtures of materials Breadth of study: 1 / 2	6D Reversible and irreversible changes	Reversible and irreversible cooking	34
			Reversible processes, reusable resources	35
	Sc4 Physical processes 2 Forces and motion Breadth of study: 1 / 2	6E Forces in action	The force of air	2
			Weight in space	22
	Sc4 Physical processes 3 Light and sound Breadth of study: 1 / 2	6F How we see things	Different mirrors	12
			Projectors	36
	Sc4 Physical processes 1 Electricity Breadth of study: 1 / 2	6G Changing circuits	Wires and bulbs	13
			Lights for your bike	14
Geography	Knowledge, skills and understanding 3 Knowledge and understanding of places 4 Knowledge and understanding of patterns and processes 5 Knowledge and understanding of environmental change and sustainable development Breadth of study: 6 / 7	14 Investigating rivers 24 Passport to the world 25 Geography and numbers	River travel in Sarawak, Borneo	15
			Recreation on the Thames	16
			Longest rivers in the world	23
	Knowledge, skills and understanding 3 Knowledge and understanding of places 4 Knowledge and understanding of patterns and processes 5 Knowledge and understanding of environmental change and sustainable development Breadth of study: 6 / 7	15 The mountain environment 24 Passport to the world 25 Geography and numbers	Mountain ranges	24
			Mountain weather	25
			The Alps	37
	Knowledge, skills and understanding 3 Knowledge and understanding of places 4 Knowledge and understanding of patterns and processes Breadth of study: 6 / 7	16 What's in the news? 24 Passport to the world 25 Geography and numbers	Spending the Euro	17
			Who's best at recycling?	26

Curriculum subject	Key Stage 2 National Curriculum programme of study	QCA Primary scheme of work	*Maths Facts* theme	Activity
Geography *(continued)*	Knowledge, skills and understanding 3 Knowledge and understanding of places 4 Knowledge and understanding of patterns and processes Breadth of study: 6 / 7	18 Connecting ourselves to the world 24 Passport to the world 25 Geography and numbers	Communicating with the world	3
			Travelling the world	18
	Knowledge, skills and understanding 3 Knowledge and understanding of places 4 Knowledge and understanding of patterns and processes 5 Knowledge and understanding of environmental change and sustainable development Breadth of study: 6 / 7	23 Investigating coasts 24 Passport to the world 25 Geography and numbers	Where land meets sea	27
			How long are their coastlines?	28
			Falling cliffs	29
History	Knowledge, skills and understanding 1 Chronological understanding 2 Knowledge and understanding of events, people and changes in the past Breadth of study: 11a	11 What was it like for children living in Victorian Britain?	How they lived	4
	Knowledge, skills and understanding 1 Chronological understanding 2 Knowledge and understanding of events, people and changes in the past Breadth of study: 11a	12 How did life change in our locality in Victorian times?	Jobs in Victorian times	5
			How trains changed the Victorians	38
	Knowledge, skills and understanding 1 Chronological understanding 2 Knowledge and understanding of events, people and changes in the past Breadth of study: 11b	13 How has life changed in Britain since 1948?	Spending the £ since 1950	19
			How the government spends its money	20
	Knowledge, skills and understanding 1 Chronological understanding 2 Knowledge and understanding of events, people and changes in the past Breadth of study: 12	14 Who were the ancient Greeks?	Famous Greeks	6
	Knowledge, skills and understanding 1 Chronological understanding 2 Knowledge and understanding of events, people and changes in the past Breadth of study: 12	15 How do we use ancient Greek ideas today?	Democracy	7
			The Modern Olympics	8
	Knowledge, skills and understanding 1 Chronological understanding 2 Knowledge and understanding of events, people and changes in the past Breadth of study: 13	16 How can we find out about the Indus Valley civilisation?	Weighing things in Harappa	30
		16 How can we find out about the Aztec civilisation?	The Aztecs in the Valley of Mexico	9
	Knowledge, skills and understanding 1 Chronological understanding 2 Knowledge and understanding of events, people and changes in the past Breadth of study: 10 / 13	19 What were the effects of Tudor exploration?	Tudor sailors	39
			A Tudor expedition	40
	Knowledge, skills and understanding 1 Chronological understanding 2 Knowledge and understanding of events, people and changes in the past Breadth of study: 11b	20 What can we learn about recent history from studying the life of a famous person?	Nelson Mandela and the struggle against apartheid	10

General guidance for Levels A, B and C in *Maths Facts* Year 6

Level A

Children should have been introduced to the following objectives:

- Use decimal notation for tenths and hundredths.
- Understand percentage as the number of parts in every 100.
- Find simple percentages of small whole-number quantities.
- Use known number facts and place value to consolidate mental addition/subtraction.
- Continue knowing by heart multiplication facts up to 10 x 10.
- Derive quickly:
  - division facts corresponding to tables up to 10 x 10;
  - squares of multiples of 10 to 100;
  - doubles of two-digit numbers;
  - doubles of multiples of 10 to 1000;
  - doubles of multiples of 100 to 10 000;
  - and the corresponding halves.
- Use known number facts and place value to consolidate mental multiplication and division.

If children experience difficulty with questions at this level provide them with:

- 1–100 number square
- multiplication square

Level B

Children should have been introduced to the following objectives:

Level A objectives and:

- Use decimal notation for tenths, hundredths and thousandths.
- Use informal pencil and paper methods to support, record or explain additions and subtractions.
- Approximate first. Use informal pencil and paper methods to support, record or explain multiplications and divisions.

If children experience difficulty with questions at this level provide them with:

- calculator

Level C

Children should have been introduced to the following objectives:

Level A and B objectives and:

- Extend written methods to column addition and subtraction of numbers involving decimals.

- Extend written methods to:
  - multiplication of ThHTU x U (short multiplication);
  - short multiplication of numbers involving decimals;
  - long multiplication of a three-digit by a two-digit integer;
  - short division of TU or HTU by U (mixed-number answers);
  - division of HTU by TU (long division, whole-number answers);
  - short division of numbers involving decimals.

If children experience difficulty with questions at this level provide them with:

- calculator

Planning a programme of work for *Maths Facts*

The *Maths Facts* Programme chart on page 18 may be used in conjunction with your long- and medium-term plans to develop a *Maths Facts* programme of work throughout the year. By following the topics allocated using the NNS *Framework for teaching mathematics from Reception to Year 6* or similar scheme of work you will ensure that the children not only have an opportunity to practise and consolidate the topic and specific objectives for a particular week but also, where appropriate, link this with other National Curriculum subjects.

Maths Facts and assessment

Maths Facts activities may be used with the whole class or with groups of children as an assessment activity. Linked to the topic that is being studied at present, *Maths Facts* will provide you with an indication of how well the children have understood the objectives being covered as well as their problem solving skills.

The assessment and record-keeping format on page 19 can be used to assess and level individual children in Attainment Target 1: *Using and applying mathematics*. By observing individual children while they undertake a *Maths Facts* activity, discussing their work with them and subsequently marking their work, you will be able to gain a good understanding of their problem solving, communicating and reasoning skills. Your judgements about an individual child's abilities can then be entered onto the assessment and record-keeping format and this will provide you with an Attainment Target 1 Level. It is envisaged that one copy of the assessment and record-keeping format would be used for your entire class.

Maths Facts Programme

Year: _______ Class: _______

Teacher: ____________________

	Week	Mathematics topic	Other National Curriculum subject and topic	*Maths Facts* activity
AUTUMN	1			
	2			
	3			
	4			
	5			
	6			
	7			
	8			
	9			
	10			
	11			
	12			
SPRING	1			
	2			
	3			
	4			
	5			
	6			
	7			
	8			
	9			
	10			
	11			
	12			
SUMMER	1			
	2			
	3			
	4			
	5			
	6			
	7			
	8			
	9			
	10			
	11			
	12			

Attainment Target 1: *Using and applying mathematics*
Assessment and record-keeping format

Year: ______ Class: ______

Teacher: ____________

LEVEL 3

Problem solving	Communicating	Reasoning
• Develop different mathematical approaches to a problem • Look for ways to overcome difficulties • Begin to make decisions and realise that results may vary according to the 'rule' used • Begin to organise work • Check results	• Discuss mathematical work • Begin to explain thinking • Use and interpret mathematical symbols and diagrams	• Understand a general statement • Investigate general statements and predictions by finding and trying out examples

LEVEL 4

Problem solving	Communicating	Reasoning
• Develop own strategies for solving problems • Use own strategies for working within mathematics • Use own strategies for applying mathematics to practical contexts	• Present information and results in a clear and organised way	• Search for solutions by trying out own ideas

GENERAL COMMENTS

LEVEL 5

Problem solving	Communicating	Reasoning
• Identify and obtain necessary information • Check results, considering whether these are sensible	• Show understanding of situations by describing them mathematically using symbols, words and diagrams	• Draw simple conclusions • Give an explanation for their reasoning

LEVEL 6

Problem solving	Communicating	Reasoning
• Carry through substantial tasks • Solve complex problems by independently breaking them down into smaller, more manageable, tasks	• Interpret, discuss and synthesise information presented in a variety of mathematical forms • Use writing to explain and inform diagrams	• Begin to give mathematical justifications

Activity 1

Problems involving 'real life'
Science 6B. Micro-organisms

Name ______________________

Date ______________________

Deadly microbes

Malaria is a disease spread by mosquitoes. It kills about 1 million people around the world each year.

Smallpox was a highly contagious disease that made people very ill and often killed them. It was eradicated by 1980.

Cholera causes severe diarrhoea and can kill people if it is not treated. It is spread by dirty drinking water.

Polio is a disease that cripples people. Due to a worldwide vaccination programme it should be eradicated by 2005.

Food poisoning is one of the most common forms of illness. Most microbes that cause it are killed by cooking the food.

Show any working on the back of this sheet.

A

1 In the 1300s, a plague called the Black Death killed $\frac{1}{4}$ of all the people in Europe. It was spread by rats. If 200 000 people were living in London at this time, how many of them died?

2 A flu epidemic in 1918–1919 killed 20 million people worldwide. Only 8·5 million people died altogether in World War I. How many more people died in the flu epidemic?

3 100 000 American soldiers died in World War I. Of these, 43 000 died of flu. What percentage is this?

4 Smallpox was eradicated by 1980. Between 1880 and 1980 Smallpox killed 500 million people. On average, how many is this each year?

B

1 Each year, 1 in 4 people in the USA suffer from food poisoning. The population of the USA is 272 million. How many suffer from food poisoning each year?

2 In the USA, 325 000 people go to hospital each year with food poisoning. Of these, 5000 die. What fraction of the people who enter hospital with food poisoning die?

3 Each year in India, there are 1500 cases of Cholera in every 100 000 people. If the population of India is 1000 million, how many people get Cholera each year?

4 In 2000, 550 million children around the world were inoculated against Polio. If there are 5500 million people in the world, what percentage were inoculated against Polio?

C

1 In the 1300s, a plague called the Black Death killed $\frac{1}{4}$ of all the people in Europe within 4 years. What fraction of the population did it kill each year?

2 In 2001, scientists found that 12 out of 1028 fruit and vegetables tested were infected with food poisoning. What fraction were infected, rounded to the nearest whole number?

3 Malaria kills 1 million people each year. 25% fewer would die if they slept under mosquito nets. How many fewer would die if they slept under mosquito nets?

4 In 2000, 550 million children were inoculated against Polio. This is about 85% of all the children in the world. Roughly how many children are there in the world?

Problems involving 'real life'
Science: 6E. Forces in action

Name ______________________

Date ______________________

The force of air

Show any working on the back of this sheet.

A

1 The biggest airship was the Hindenburg. This carried 75 passengers and 25 crew. What was the ratio of passengers to crew?

2 In the sport of skydiving, people jump from an aeroplane at a height of 3550 m and perform aerobatics until they open their parachutes at a height of 600 m. How far do they fall before opening their parachutes?

3 In 1982, a man attached 45 helium-filled balloons to a deck chair and rose almost 5000 m into the sky. He then shot 10 of them and sailed back down to Earth. What fraction of his balloons did he shoot?

4 The Cannes Resort boat can take 2 people paragliding at a time. It makes 3 trips an hour, 8 hours a day. How many people can it take in 7 days?

B

1 The first airline service started in 1909 using airships. In 4 years it carried 34 000 passengers. On average, how many passengers was this each year?

2 The first flight by a hydrogen balloon was in 1783 in Paris. The crash of the airship Hindenburg, 154 years later, effectively ended commercial passenger airships. In what year did it crash?

3 The first recorded parachute jump was in Spain in 852 AD when a man jumped off a tower wearing a huge cloak and survived! In 1466 Leonardo da Vinci designed the first parachute. How many years later was this?

4 The Shoalhaven Parachute Club has 532 members. Last year, on average, each member made 8 jumps. How many jumps was this in total?

C

1 Sophia is on a hang-gliding holiday. She makes 7 flights. They last for 46 min, 52 min, 1 hr 7 min, 49 min, 50 min, 35 min and 1 hr 12 min. What is her average flight time?

2 The worst airship disaster was in 1933 when 73 people were killed and 3 survived. Approximately what fraction survived?

3 In 2001, a man made 500 parachute jumps in 24 hours. How long did each parachute jump last on average, to the nearest minute?

4 In 1998 a Swiss balloonist set a record for the longest non-stop flight by an aircraft. He stayed airborne for almost 14 040 minutes. How many days and hours was this?

Activity 3

Problems involving 'real life'
Geography: 18. Connecting ourselves to the world

Name ______________________

Date ______________________

Communicating with the world

58% of people in France own telephones.

Number for every 1000 people	Australia	Belgium	France	Greece	Italy	Japan	Spain	Turkey	UK	USA
Computers	366	249	234	73	158	228	127	20	283	450
Mobile phones	446	549	494	559	737	449	306	125	670	316
Daily newspapers	258	321	237	144	105	576	104	44	351	228
Radios	1291	774	891	418	802	912	312	162	1429	2122
Telephones	524	499	580	528	462	558	421	278	567	673
Televisions	489	453	591	206	437	681	402	181	439	817

Show any working on the back of this sheet.

A

1. Out of every 1000 people, 125 people in Turkey have mobile phones, and 670 people in the UK have them. How many more have them in the UK?
2. In France, how many more people have mobile phones than computers per 1000 people?
3. How many mobile phones do 2000 people in the UK own altogether?
4. In which two countries do almost half as many people have computers as telephones?

B

1. Out of every 500 people in France, how many own mobile phones?
2. What percentage of people in Belgium have radios?
3. Written as a fraction, what is the proportion of people with mobile phones in Turkey?
4. Altogether, how many computers do 5000 people in the USA own?

C

1. How many more radios do 1000 people in the USA own than in Australia?
2. In which country do 23·9% more of the population own computers than in Spain?
3. How many daily newspapers do 125 people buy altogether in Japan?
4. What is the ratio of people who buy daily newspapers in Greece to those who own a telephone?

Problems involving 'real life'
History: 11. What was it like for children living in Victorian Britain?

Name ______________________

Date ______________________

How they lived

The table below shows the number of rooms that people had in their houses during Victorian times.

Percentage of the population in houses with:

	1 room (%)	2 rooms (%)	3 rooms (%)	4 rooms (%)	5 rooms (%)	6 rooms (%)	More than 6 rooms (%)
1841	**30·6**	**37·4**	**11·9**	**5·4**	**3·1**	**2·6**	**9·0**
1861	**26·6**	**38·2**	**12·7**	**6·4**	**3·7**	**2·9**	**9·5**
1881	**18·0**	**39·5**	**16·1**	**7·6**	**4·2**	**3·2**	**11·4**
1901	**11·0**	**39·5**	**19·9**	**9·1**	**4·9**	**3·5**	**12·1**

Show any working on the back of this sheet.

A

1. In 1841, 30·6% of the population lived in houses with 1 room. As a percentage, how many fewer lived in 1 room houses in 1901?
2. In 1841, 37·4% of the population lived in houses with 2 rooms. What percentage of the population did not live in a house with 2 rooms?
3. What percentage of the population lived in houses with 3 or more rooms in 1861?
4. In 1901, did more people live in houses with 3 or more rooms or in houses with 1 or 2 rooms? How many percent more?

B

1. The population of Edinburgh in 1881 was 295 000. How many of these people lived in 1 room houses?
2. In 1861, 90 174 people in Manchester lived in houses with only 1 room. 20 years later, 7015 fewer people lived in 1 room houses. How many people lived in 1 room houses 20 years later?
3. 166 000 people lived in Edinburgh in 1841. How many of them lived in houses with more than 6 rooms?
4. In 1861, 339 000 people lived in Manchester. 90 174 lived in 1 room houses. How many lived in houses with more than 1 room?

C

1. In 1901 there were 762 000 people living in Glasgow. Roughly how many lived in 3 room houses?
2. Manchester had a population of 339 000 people in 1861. How many of them lived in houses with more than 6 rooms?
3. The population of Edinburgh in 1881 was 295 000. How many more people lived in 5 room houses than 6 room houses?
4. In Glasgow, in 1881, 94 507 people lived in 3 room houses. 137 358 more people lived in 2 room houses. How many people lived in 2 room houses?

Problems involving 'real life'
History: 12. How did life change in our locality in Victorian times?

Name ______________________

Date ______________________

Jobs in Victorian times

The table below shows the types of jobs that people living in a city with 10 000 working men (M) and 10 000 working women (W) would have done in Victorian times.

	Professional (e.g. doctors, teachers)		***Domestic service*** (e.g. maids, cooks)		***Commerce*** (e.g. shop-keepers)		***Farming and fishing*** (e.g. farmers, fisherman)		***Industry*** (e.g. factory workers)	
	M	W	M	W	M	W	M	W	M	W
1841	**453**	**57**	**203**	**3160**	**1509**	**287**	**444**	**37**	**7391**	**6459**
1861	**483**	**114**	**150**	**2340**	**1647**	**372**	**303**	**27**	**7417**	**7147**
1881	**518**	**463**	**113**	**2066**	**1971**	**231**	**69**	**21**	**7329**	**7219**
1901	**456**	**530**	**74**	**2161**	**2384**	**765**	**36**	**16**	**7050**	**6528**

Show any working on the back of this sheet.

A 1 How many fewer men were in domestic service in 1901 than in 1841?

2 How many men and women altogether were in farming and fishing in 1861?

3 There were more men than women in commerce in 1881. How many more?

4 Out of 10 000 working men, how many were not in professional jobs in 1861?

B 1 How many more women were in domestic service in 1841 than men?

2 There were fewer women than men in industry in 1901. How many fewer?

3 Which column shows the greatest increase in number between 1841 and 1901?

4 What percentage of women were working in industry in 1881?

C 1 How many more men than women worked in industry in 1861?

2 More men worked in commerce than in professional jobs in 1901. How many more?

3 What was the ratio of men to women in farming and fishing in 1841?

4 Of the 20 000 people working in 1881, what percentage of men and women combined worked in commerce?

Activity 6

Problems involving 'real life'
History: 14. Who were the ancient Greeks?

Name ______________________

Date ______________________

Famous Greeks

Show any working on the back of this sheet.

1. Archimedes made an important discovery one day in his bath; he jumped out and ran through the town shouting 'Eureka'. He lived from 287 BC to 212 BC. For how long did he live?
2. Pythagoras was a famous mathematician; he died in 480 BC at the age of 90. In which year was he born?
3. Socrates was a famous Greek philosopher. He lived from 469 BC to 399 BC. For how many years did he live?
4. Alexander the Great was born in 356 BC. He became king at the age of 20. In which year did he become king?

1. Alexander the Great was born in late 356 BC. He conquered the largest empire in the ancient world and died early in 323 BC. How old was he when he died?
2. In 490 BC, 10 000 Greeks fought the Persian army at the Battle of Marathon. About 200 Greeks were killed and 6000 Persians. How many Persians were killed for each Greek?
3. Hippocrates was a doctor whose teachings spread throughout the ancient world. All doctors today still take the Hippocratic oath promising to do good. Hippocrates died in 377 BC at the age of 83. In which year was he born?
4. Plato was a famous Athenian philosopher. He was born in 429 BC and lived for 82 years. In which year did he die?

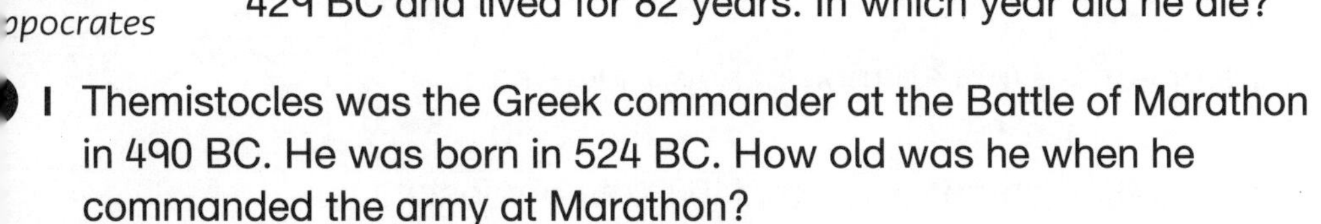

1. Themistocles was the Greek commander at the Battle of Marathon in 490 BC. He was born in 524 BC. How old was he when he commanded the army at Marathon?
2. Alexander the Great invaded Asia with 5000 cavalry and 30 000 infantry. What fraction of the army was cavalry?
3. Aristotle was an Athenian philosopher born in 384 BC. He taught Alexander the Great for 3 years before returning to Athens in 335 BC. How old was he when he started teaching Alexander?
4. Aristophanes was a famous Greek writer of comic plays. He wrote 40 plays of which only 11 survive. What percentage of his plays survives?

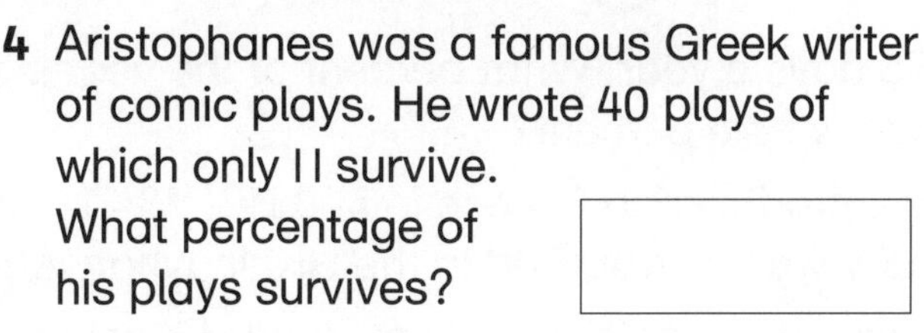

Problems involving 'real life'
History: 15. How do we use ancient Greek ideas today?

Name ______________________

Date ______________________

Democracy

The ancient Greeks invented the system of government called Democracy. Under this system, all citizens have a say in the running of their country. In the UK, we do this by voting for members of parliament (MPs). There are 659 MPs. MPs belong to different groups called parties.

Show any working on the back of this sheet

A

1 There are 659 MPs. If 118 of these are women, how many are men?

2 There are 659 MPs. If 412 of these belong to the Labour Party, how many belong to other parties?

3 If 396 MPs vote for a law and 137 vote against it, how many MPs have voted altogether?

4 Elections to parliament are held roughly every 5 years. If someone has been an MP for 28 years, how many times have they been elected?

B

1 Parliament works for 155 days a year. Approximately how many weeks is this?

2 If a member of parliament earns £4593 a month, how much is this a year?

3 There are 659 MPs. If 334 MPs vote for a law and 168 vote against it, how many MPs did not vote?

4 To pass a law, more than half the MPs present that day must vote 'yes'. If all 659 MPs are present, how many must vote 'yes' for a law to pass?

C

1 Parliament works for 36 hours a week, 155 days a year. How many hours is this a year?

2 Parliament works 155 days a year. What percent of the year is this, rounded to the nearest whole percent?

3 Democracy was first introduced in Greece in 508 BC. 2340 years later, the principle of democracy was established in the UK. In what year was this?

4 658 MPs vote on a new law. $\frac{4}{7}$ of them vote for it, and $\frac{3}{7}$ vote against it. How many MPs vote for the new law?

Problems involving 'real life'
History: 15. How do we use ancient Greek ideas today?

Name ______________________

Date ______________________

The Modern Olympics

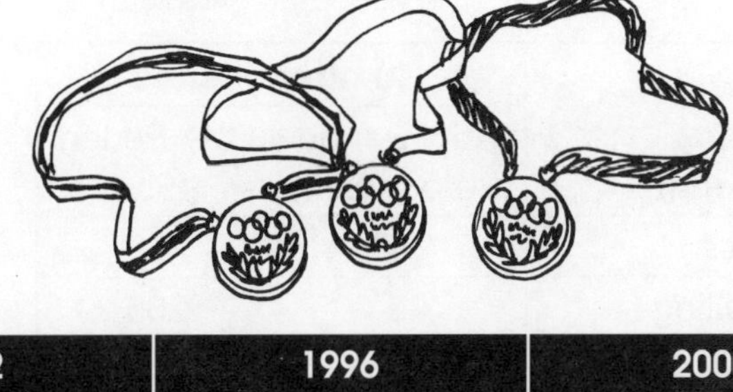

	1992 Barcelona, Spain			1996 Atlanta, USA			2000 Sydney, Australia		
	Gold	Silver	Bronze	Gold	Silver	Bronze	Gold	Silver	Bronze
Australia	7	9	11	9	9	23	16	25	17
China	16	22	16	16	22	12	28	16	15
Germany	33	21	28	20	18	27	13	17	26
Great Britain	5	3	12	1	8	6	11	10	7
Russia	45	38	29	26	21	16	32	28	28
USA	37	34	37	44	32	25	40	24	33
All other countries combined	117	130	165	156	172	162	161	169	201

Show any working on the back of this sheet.

A
1 How many gold medals did Russia win in these three Olympic games?

2 Germany won 21 silver medals in Barcelona. What fraction of this number of silver medals did they win in Atlanta?

3 What percentage of the medals that Great Britain won in the Barcelona Olympics were gold?

4 How many more medals did Australia win in the 2000 Olympics than Great Britain?

B
1 How many gold medals altogether were won at the Barcelona Olympics?

2 How many medals did China win altogether in these three Olympic games?

3 What was the ratio of gold medals won by Australia, China and the USA at the 2000 Olympics?

4 At which Olympics did the 6 named countries in the table win more than half the gold medals?

C
1 What fraction of the gold medals awarded at the 1992 Olympics did Great Britain win?

2 Which named country won the most medals at these three Olympic games?

3 Which named country at which Olympics won gold, silver and bronze medals in the ratio 8 : 11 : 6?

4 How many more medals altogether did Russia win than Germany in these three Olympics?

Problems involving 'real life'
History: 16. How can we find out about the Aztec civilisation?

Name ______________________

Date ______________________

The Aztecs in the Valley of Mexico

Type of settlement	Number of sites	
	Early Period (Before 1325)	Late Period (1519)
Hamlet	258	986
Small village	15	265
Large village	4	88
Regional centre	14	41
Capital city	0	2
Religious centre	1	59
Other sites	106	195

Show any working on the back of this sheet

A 1 How many fewer regional centres were there in the Early Period than in the Late Period?

2 By how many times did the number of large villages increase between the Early Period and the Late Period?

3 How many hamlets, small villages and large villages were there in the Early Period?

4 The population in the Early Period was 175 000. By the Late Period it had increased to 920 000 people. By how many people had it increased?

B 1 How many sites where there altogether in the Early Period?

2 How many more hamlets were there in the Late Period than in the Early Period?

3 How many more hamlets were there in the Late Period than small and large villages combined?

4 Roughly $\frac{5}{8}$ of the Early Period sites were one type of settlement, what type was this?

C 1 How many more sites were there in the Late Period than in the Early Period?

2 In the Late Period almost $\frac{1}{40}$ of the sites were of one particular type. What type was this?

3 Excluding capital cities, what type of settlement shows the greatest percentage increase between the Early and Late Periods?

4 One type of settlement has a ratio of 3 : 53 between the numbers in the Early Period and in the Late Period. Which type of settlement is this?

Problems involving 'real life'
History: 20. What can we learn about recent history from studying the life of a famous person?

Name ______________________

Date ______________________

Nelson Mandela and the struggle against apartheid

"I have cherished the ideal of a democratic and free society in which all persons live together in harmony and with equal opportunities ... If needs be, it is an ideal for which I am prepared to die."

South Africa in 1978	Black	White
Population	81%	19%
Land allocation	13%	87%
Ratio of average earnings	1	14
1 doctor for every	44 000	400
Money spent on education for each child each year	£30	£450
1 teacher for every	60 children	22 children

Show any working on the back of this sheet.

A

1 Nelson Mandela was born in Transkei, South Africa in July 1918. He became president of South Africa in May 1994. How old was he when he became president?

2 In 1978, how much more money was spent on educating a white child each year than a black child?

3 Nelson Mandela was sent to prison in 1962. He was released from prison in 1990. For how many years was he imprisoned?

4 In 1978, of every 100 hectares of land, how many more hectares did the white population own than the black population?

B

1 On 5 December 1956, Nelson Mandela was arrested for treason. It was not until 29 March 1961 that his trial began. Approximately how many months after his arrest did the trial begin?

2 In 1960, 69 people were killed and 187 people wounded during a demonstration in a township called Sharpville. How many people were killed or wounded altogether?

3 In 1978 the population of South Africa was 24 million. If 19% were white, how many people were white?

4 In 1978 the population of South Africa was 24 million. How many people were black?

C

1 Nelson Mandela was released from jail on 11 February 1990. He became the president of South Africa on 10 May 1994. How long in years, months and days after leaving jail did he become president?

2 In 1978, how many black children were educated for the same cost as one white child?

3 In 1978 there was one doctor for every 44 000 black people. How many doctors were there for every 44 000 white people?

4 In 1978 for every 1000 white babies born, 27 would die before their 1st birthday. For every 1000 black babies born this number rose to 300. What is this difference as a percentage?

Problems involving money
Science: 6B. Micro-organisms

Name ____________________

Date ____________________

Friendly microbes

All the food items below are made with the help of microbes.

Show any working on the back of this sheet

A

1 6 fruit buns cost 78p. How much does each bun cost?

2 Is a kilogram of Cheddar or a kilogram of Brie more expensive?

3 How much does a kilogram of Greek yoghurt cost?

4 What is the total cost of 3 wholemeal loaves of bread and 2 white loaves?

B

1 What is the total cost of all the items in the picture?

2 How much would it cost to buy 54 fruit buns for a party?

3 What is the cost of a kilogram of low fat yoghurt?

4 500 g of bio yoghurt costs 90p. How much does 150 g cost?

C

1 How much does one kilogram of Stilton cost?

2 What is the ratio of the cost of white bread to wholemeal bread?

3 How much does $1\frac{3}{4}$ kg of Stilton cost?

4 How much Edam cheese can you buy for £2?

Problems involving money
Science: 6F. How we see things

Name ____________________

Date ____________________

Different mirrors

Show any working on the back of this sheet.

A
1 Tom needs a shaving mirror. They vary in price from £3.27 up to £27.99. What is the difference in price between the cheapest and the most expensive?

2 Mr. and Mrs. Alton are furnishing their house. They spend £476 on two identical mirrors. How much does each one cost?

3 The Waltons cannot see approaching traffic as they come out of their drive onto the road, so they put up two mirrors costing £165.70 each. What is the total cost of the two mirrors?

4 Rajani's store is installing security mirrors in each aisle. They cost £47 each and they need 6 of them. How much will this cost them?

B
1 The Betterwear Clothes Shop needs some new mirrors. They buy four big ones at £96.45 each for the shop, and two smaller ones at £37.39 each for the changing rooms. How much do they spend?

2 Birrilley Primary School buys a set of 30 small mirrors to teach symmetry. If the set costs £10.50, how much does each mirror cost?

3 Imran buys a periscope in a sale. He gets 20% off the normal price of £26.40. How much does he pay?

4 The rear view mirror in Jane's car fell off and broke. A new one costs £15.87 and the garage charges £22.46 to fit it. How much change does she get from £50?

C
1 This Sunday, Mike's Mirrors is offering £12 off all mirrors over £50. They sell 12 mirrors originally costing £60 each, 6 originally costing £78 each and 4 originally costing £116 each. How much money do they take on Sunday?

2 Gillian's Gym buys 45 m^2 of mirror for £864. How much is this per square metre?

3 The Grand Hotel is redecorating and needs 120 mirrors. The first 50 mirrors cost £27 each, the next 50 cost 20% less than the full price and the remaining ones cost 30% less. What is the total bill?

4 Birrilley Primary School is buying 7 overhead projectors. They cost £190 each, but as they are a school they do not pay VAT and get a discount of 17.5%. How much do they pay?

Problems involving money
Science: 6G. Changing circuits

Name ______________________

Date ______________________

Wires and bulbs

1·5 mm diameter wire
62p a metre
used for light circuits

2·5 mm diameter wire
£1.57 a metre
used for socket circuits

6·5 mm diameter wire
£4.30 a metre
used for electric cookers

40W bulb uses 0.32p of electricity an hour

60W bulb uses 0.48p of electricity an hour

100W bulb uses 0.8p of electricity an hour

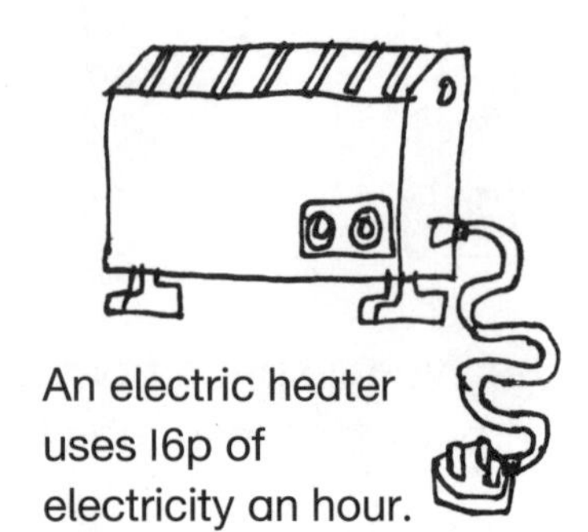

An electric heater uses 16p of electricity an hour.

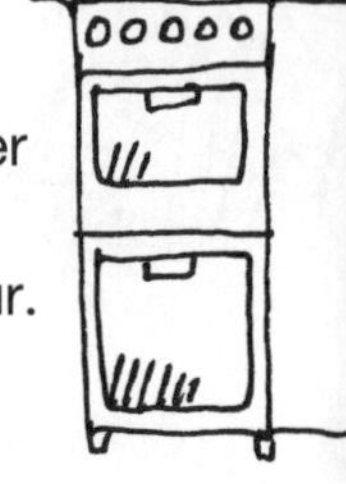

An electric cooker uses £1.20 of electricity an hour.

Show any working on the back of this sheet

A

1 How much does 5 m of 1·5 mm wire cost?

2 How much does it cost to run a 60W bulb for 10 hours?

3 Steve is moving his electric cooker and needs 1·5 m of 6·5 mm wire. How much does this cost?

4 What is the cost of electricity to run an electric heater for 5 hours?

B

1 How much does it cost to buy 14 m of 1·5 mm wire?

2 If you run a 60W bulb for 5 hours every evening, how much does it cost for a 7 day week?

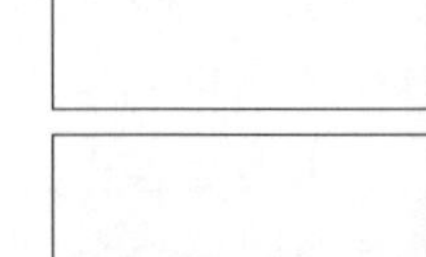

3 How many metres of 2·5 mm wire can you buy for £7.85?

4 Jo is replacing his gas cooker with an electric cooker. He needs 23 m of 6·5 mm wire. What does this cost him?

C

1 Samantha uses an electric hair dryer every day. This uses 1·6p of electricity each day. How much does she spend on drying her hair in a 365 day year?

2 In the Millers' house there are two 40W bulbs which run for 1 hour each day, four 60W bulbs which run for 5 hours each day and one 100W bulb which runs for 3 hours each day. How much does this cost each week?

3 Lee is rewiring his house and needs 64 m of 2·5 mm wire. What does this cost him?

4 You can run a 40W bulb for 100 hours on 32p of electricity. For how many hours can you run a 40W bulb on £1 of electricity?

Problems involving money
Science: 6G. Changing circuits

Name ____________________

Date ____________________

ights for your bike

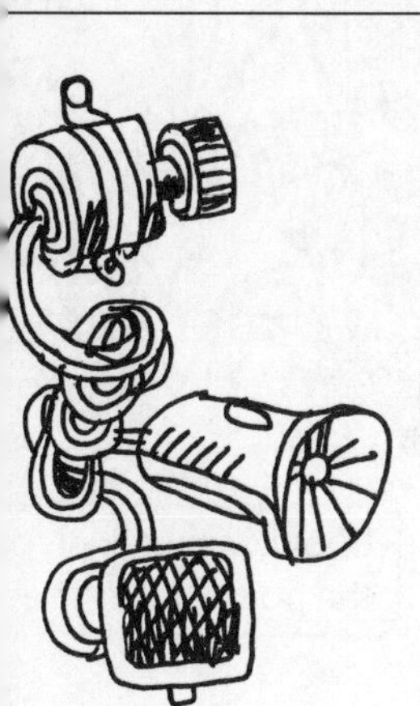

Dynamo system	Battery lights
Dynamo £16*	Halogen front light £14*
Standard front light £4.16	Ordinary front light £6.55
Extra bright front light £5.30	Halogen rear light £6*
Standard rear light £2.35	Ordinary rear light £3.10
Extra bright rear light £3.34	

*Prices DO NOT include VAT at 17·5%

Show any working on the back of this sheet.

1 Ahmed has bought a new set of front and rear lights. He needs 2·5 metres of wire to connect them to the dynamo. If the wire costs 18p a metre, how much does the wire cost?

2 A standard rear light for a dynamo system is £2.35. How much more expensive is an extra bright rear light?

3 Sanjay has been given a dynamo for his bike. He buys an extra bright front light and an extra bright rear light, and some wire to connect them to the dynamo. If the wire costs 40p, how much does he pay?

4 How much more expensive are a set of extra bright front and rear lights for a dynamo system than a standard set?

1 Sven buys battery-powered halogen front and rear lights. How much VAT does he have to pay at 17·5%?

2 Peter has lights powered by a dynamo. When he is stationary at traffic lights the lights go out, so he buys a battery halogen rear light, how much does he pay, with VAT?

3 Declan buys a dynamo and a set of standard front and rear lights. How much does this cost him including VAT?

4 John buys a halogen front light for his bike. What is the total cost, with VAT?

1 How much change does Leroy get from £20 after buying a dynamo and paying the VAT?

2 Including VAT, how much more expensive are a set of halogen front and rear lights than a set of ordinary battery front and rear lights?

3 The cost of a standard rear light for a dynamo system is £2.35 including VAT. How much does it cost without VAT?

4 Which is more expensive, a dynamo (+ VAT) and set of extra bright front and rear lights, or halogen front and rear lights (+ VAT) with batteries costing £4? How much more expensive?

Problems involving money
Geography: 14. Investigating rivers

Name ______________________

Date ______________________

River travel in Sarawak, Borneo

Most of Borneo is covered in jungle. There are not many roads and the most convenient way to travel is by boat on the rivers. On large rivers, modern express boats travel very fast, but on smaller rivers, travel is by open long boat.

Belaga

Kapit

Sibu

Show any working on the back of this sheet

A

1. The fare on the express boat from Sibu to Kapit is £4.25 in First Class and £3.33 in Tourist Class. How much more expensive is First Class than Tourist Class?
2. An Economy fare from Sibu to Kapit is £2.75. How much does it cost for 4 people to travel?
3. Economy fares cost £2.75 and Tourist fares cost £3.33. How much do 4 adults save altogether if they travel in Economy rather than Tourist Class?
4. A First Class fare from Sibu to Kapit costs £4.25. If children travel for 60% of the adult fare, how much does a First Class child's fare cost?

B

1. The fare on the express boat from Sibu to Kapit is £4.25 in First Class, £3.33 in Tourist Class and £2.75 in Economy Class. There are 12 seats in First Class, 24 in Tourist and 40 in Economy. If the boat is full with adults, how much money is this?
2. A First Class ticket from Sibu to Kapit is £4.25. A First Class ticket from Kapit upriver to Belaga is 40% more expensive than this. How much is the ticket from Kapit to Belaga?
3. Travelling by Tourist Class, it costs £5.35 to travel by boat from the capital Kuching to Sibu, £3.33 from Sibu to Kapit and £4.66 from Kapit to Belaga. How much does it cost to travel from Kuching to Belaga and back again?
4. It takes 3 days to travel by boat from Kuching to Belaga. If the travel costs £16.15 and the hotels cost £18.76 and £23.87 per person, what is the total cost for 2 people?

C

1. The currency in Sarawak is called the Ringit. 6 Ringits equal £1. A First Class ticket from Sibu to Kapit is £4.25. How many Ringits is this?
2. Above Belaga, all travel is by open long boat. If it costs 200 Ringits a day to hire a long boat, and 6 Ringits equal £1, how many pounds does it cost to hire a long boat for 3 days?
3. 6 Ringits equal £1. If you spend 5874 Ringits on a river adventure in Sarawak, how much is this in pounds?
4. Petrol for the long boats becomes more expensive the further you travel upriver. If it costs 48p a litre in Sibu and 12.5% more in Belaga, how much does it cost for 6 litres in Belaga?

Problems involving money

Geography: 14. Investigating rivers

Name ______________________

Date ______________________

Recreation on the Thames

Show any working on the back of this sheet.

1. It costs £261 a day to hire a boat carrying 12 people at the weekend, but only £209 a day during the week. How much cheaper is it during the week?
2. At the weekend, it costs £261 to hire a boat for a day and £144 for half a day. How much more expensive is it to hire a boat for the day?
3. In March, it costs £744 to hire a boat which sleeps 6 people for a week. How much does it cost to hire the boat for a fortnight?
4. A 2 hour boat trip from Walton to Hampton Court costs £6.50 each way for adults and half of this for children. How much does the return trip cost for 2 adults and 2 children?

1. It costs £23 an hour to hire a boat. How much would it cost to hire it for 6 hours?
2. A $1\frac{1}{2}$ hour boat trip from Walton to Hampton Court costs £5.75 for adults and £2.90 for children, one way. How much does a one way trip cost for 2 adults and 3 children?
3. It costs £23 an hour to hire a boat. It costs £134 a day to hire the same boat. If you want the boat for 8 hours, how much cheaper is it to hire it by the day than by the hour?
4. In March, it costs £744 to hire a boat which sleeps 6 people for a week. It costs £389 more to hire the same boat in August. What is the price to hire the boat in August?

1. It costs £261 to hire a boat carrying 12 people for a day. How much is this per person?
2. Membership of an angling club costs £31.50 for adults and £15.75 for children for the season. The season runs from 16th June to 16th March. How much is this per month for 1 adult and 1 child?
3. A Disco Cruise with fish and chip dinner on a boat on the Thames costs £24.50 per person. If the minimum number of people needed is 36, what is the minimum amount of money the boat takes?
4. Membership of an angling club costs £31.50 for adults and £15.75 for children. If the club has 230 adults and 40 children, how much money is this?

Activity **17**

Problems involving money
Geography: 16. What's in the news?

Name ____________________

Date ____________________

Spending the Euro

1st January, 2003

The Euro Celebrates its 1st Birthday

A year ago began a grand experiment never tried before. Out went the Italian Lira, the French Franc, the German Deutschmark and 8 other currencies, all to be replaced by one currency – the Euro. How have people in these countries coped with the change to a completely new form of money? For the first two months after the Euro was introduced, people used it alongside their own currencies, but from the 1st March, 2002, they have used only the Euro.

1 Euro (€) =

Austrian Shilling	Belgian Franc	Dutch Florin	Finnish Mark	French Franc	German Deutschmark	Greek Drachma	Irish Pound	Italian Lira	Portuguese Escudo	Spanish Peseta
13·76 Sh	**40·34** BFr	**2·2** Fl	**5·95** Fmk	**6·56** FFr	**1·96** DM	**340** Dr	**0·79** I£	**1936** L	**200·5** Esc	**166·4** Pta

Show any working on the back of this sheet.

A
1. 2 Euros equalled how many Irish Pounds?
2. If 1 kg of oranges cost 680 Greek Drachma, how many Euros do they cost?
3. How many Finnish Marks were the same as 10 Euros?
4. 11 Dutch Florins equalled how many Euros?

B
1. In January 2002, a T-shirt cost €9. How many Austrian Shillings was this?
2. If a television cost 196 German Deutschmarks in February 2002, how many Euros was this?
3. A computer game cost €40 in February 2002. How many Portuguese Escudos was this?
4. 1 Euro = 100 cents (c). How many Belgian Francs were there in 50 c?

C
1. If a box of chocolates cost 1000 Greek Drachma, how many Euros does it cost to the nearest cent?
2. How many French Francs were there in €8.50?
3. In February 2002, a cinema ticket cost 9680 Italian Lira. How many Euros did it cost?
4. If a book cost €14 in January 2002, how many Spanish Pesetas was this?

Problems involving money
Geography: 18. Connecting ourselves to the world

Name ____________________

Date ____________________

ravelling the world

lorth America
Return fare from London to:
New York **£196**
Boston **£204**
ancouver **£287**
Los ngeles **£269**

Australia and New Zealand
Return fare from London to:
Sydney **£563**
Melbourne **£571**
Perth **£524**
Auckland **£589**

Show any working on the back of this sheet.

1 What is the cost for 4 people flying to Boston?

2 How much more expensive is it to fly to Singapore than to Bangkok?

3 Last week James flew to New York. This week he flew to Los Angeles. How much is this altogether?

4 Where can you fly to for half the cost of a flight to Delhi?

1 Which city is the 7th cheapest to fly to?

2 Cut Price Flights has cut all fares to Asia by 20%. How much does it now cost for a ticket to Singapore?

3 It costs two people £538 altogether to fly to one of the above cities. Which city is this?

4 Padmi flies to New York once a month on business. How much does this cost her a year?

1 In the last 12 months, Tony has flown to Hong Kong, Vancouver, Nairobi and Sydney. How much has this cost him altogether?

2 If children get a 25% reduction, how much does it cost for 2 adults and 2 children to fly to Cape Town?

3 Mr. and Mrs. Morton fly to Cape Town. They stay 13 nights in a hotel costing £87 a night. How much do their flights and hotel cost altogether?

4 18 members of the Wanderers Rugby Club fly to Auckland. As they are a large group they receive a 15% reduction on their fares. What is the total cost of their flights?

Problems involving money
History: 13. How has life changed in Britain since 1948?

Name ______________________

Date ______________________

Spending the £ since 1950

The tables below show the changes in how people in the UK spent their income between 1950 and 2000.

How much money most people spent in a year (£)

1950	1960	1970	1980	1990	2000
£189	£324	£564	£2433	£5864	£10 070

What most people spent their money on (%)

	Food	Alcohol and tobacco	Durable goods	Housing, fuel and light	Clothing	Travel and communication	Recreation and leisure	Other expenses
1950	25·1	15·9	5·2	12·7	11·2	5·7	16·3	7·9
1960	25·0	12·3	8·4	14·2	9·7	6·9	17·7	5·8
1970	20·3	12·9	7·4	18·0	8·5	9·7	19·1	4·1
1980	16·7	10·8	10·0	18·3	7·2	11·7	20·5	4·8
1990	12·5	4·4	5·9	16·4	6·3	17·3	22·9	14·3
2000	10·1	4·2	5·9	18·0	5·9	17·0	23·6	15·3

Show any working on the back of this sheet.

A

1 By what percent did spending on food fall between 1950 and 2000?

2 5.7% of income was spent on travel and communication in 1950. How many more percent was spent on this in 2000?

3 How many more pounds did most people spend altogether in 1960 than in 1950?

4 In 1980, 10% of most people's spending was on durable goods. How many pounds did they spend on durable goods?

B

1 In 1990 most people spent £961.70 on housing, fuel and light. They spent £1812.60 on this in 2000. How much more did they spend in 2000?

2 In 1970, how many pounds did most people spend on clothing?

3 How many pounds did most people spend on food in 1960?

4 Which type of spending shows the greatest percentage increase between 1950 and 2000?

C

1 In 2000, how many pounds did most people spend on travel and communication?

2 How many more pounds did most people spend on durable goods in 1970 than in 1960?

3 In 1990 most people spent £1342.86 on recreation and leisure. In 2000 they spent £1033.66 more. How much did they spend in 2000?

4 How many more pounds did most people spend on food in 2000 than in 1990?

Problems involving money

History: 13. How has life changed in Britain since 1948?

Name ______________________

Date ______________________

How the government spends its money

he government spends most of its money on education, health, housing and enefit payments to the unemployed, sick and retired.

his table shows how much the government spent in different years from 1950 to 2000.

	1950 (£ million)	**1960** (£ million)	**1970** (£ million)	**1980** (£ million)	**1990** (£ million)	**2000** (£ million)
Benefit payments	415·1	1009·3	2708	15 300	39 093	51 296
Education	288·0	926·8	2638	12 376	26 728	40 889
Health	415·9	902·2	2071	11 958	27 902	53 039
Housing	67·7	494·6	1339	7025	5631	3116

Show any working on the back of this sheet.

A

1. In 1970 the government spent £1339 million on housing. They spent £1299 million more on another type of spending. What type of spending was this?
2. How much more did the government spend on education in 2000 than in 1950?
3. Which type of spending almost doubled between 1990 and 2000?
4. In 1960, how much more did the government spend on education than on health?

B

1. Which type of spending showed an increase of £23 793 million between 1980 and 1990?
2. How much did the government spend altogether on benefit payments, education, health and housing in 1980?
3. Was the difference in spending between health and education greater in 1970 or 1980?
4. Which type of spending increased by about 10 times in 20 years?

C

1. One type of spending was $2\frac{1}{3}$ times greater in 1990 than in 1980. Which type of spending is this?
2. In 2000, which type of spending was almost 16·5 times as much as housing?
3. How much more did the government spend altogether on benefit payments, education, health and housing in 2000 than in 1950?
4. Which type of spending increased by £14 161 million in 10 years? Between which years did this happen?

Problems involving measures
Science: 6C. More about dissolving

Name ______________________

Date ______________________

Dissolving different foodstuffs

The pupils in 6F tested how easily different foodstuffs dissolved in water. They dissolved 1 teaspoon of each of the following in glasses of water while stirring. The table below shows their results.

Time to dissolve

	Instant coffee	Salt	Sugar	Artificial sweetener	Honey	Golden syrup	Treacle
Ice cold (0°C)	2 sec	12 sec	45 sec	15 sec	14 min 50 sec	12 min 30 sec	16 min 15 sec
Room temp (20°C)	1 sec	8 sec	11 sec	9 sec	10 min 50 sec	8 min 15 sec	11 min 40 sec
Hand warm (40°C)	1 sec	5 sec	6 sec	4 sec	6 min 15 sec	5 min 25 sec	8 min 10 sec

Show any working on the back of this sheet

A
1. What takes roughly four times longer to dissolve in ice cold water than at room temperature?
2. What type of food takes twice as long to dissolve at 0°C than at 40°C?
3. How many seconds did it take for the treacle to dissolve in 40°C water?
4. Honey takes 10 min 50 sec to dissolve at 20°C. What type of food takes half this time, and at what temperature?

B
1. What takes 11 min 45 sec longer than sugar to dissolve in ice cold water?
2. What food at what temperature takes 2 min 45 sec longer to dissolve than golden syrup at 40°C?
3. What type of food takes 7·5 times longer to dissolve at 0°C than at 40°C?
4. How many seconds did it take for the honey to dissolve at 0°C?

C
1. What food at what temperature takes twice as long to dissolve as honey at 40°C?
2. What takes 45 times as long to dissolve as sugar at 20°C?
3. It takes treacle 16 min and 15 sec to dissolve in ice cold water. What takes $\frac{1}{3}$ of this time and at what temperature?
4. What is the ratio of the time it takes for treacle to dissolve at 20°C and at 40°C?

Problems involving measures
Science: 6E. Forces in action

Name ____________________

Date ____________________

Weight in space

Gravity is the force that pulls things together. The heavier the objects the stronger the force. The force of gravity is therefore bigger on larger planets than on smaller ones. The table below shows how much 100 kg on Earth would weigh elsewhere in space.

Planet or Star	Sun	Mercury	Venus	Earth	Moon	Mars	Jupiter	Saturn	Uranus	Neptune	Pluto
Weight (kg)	2780	27	86	100	17	37	264	117	92	144	6.6

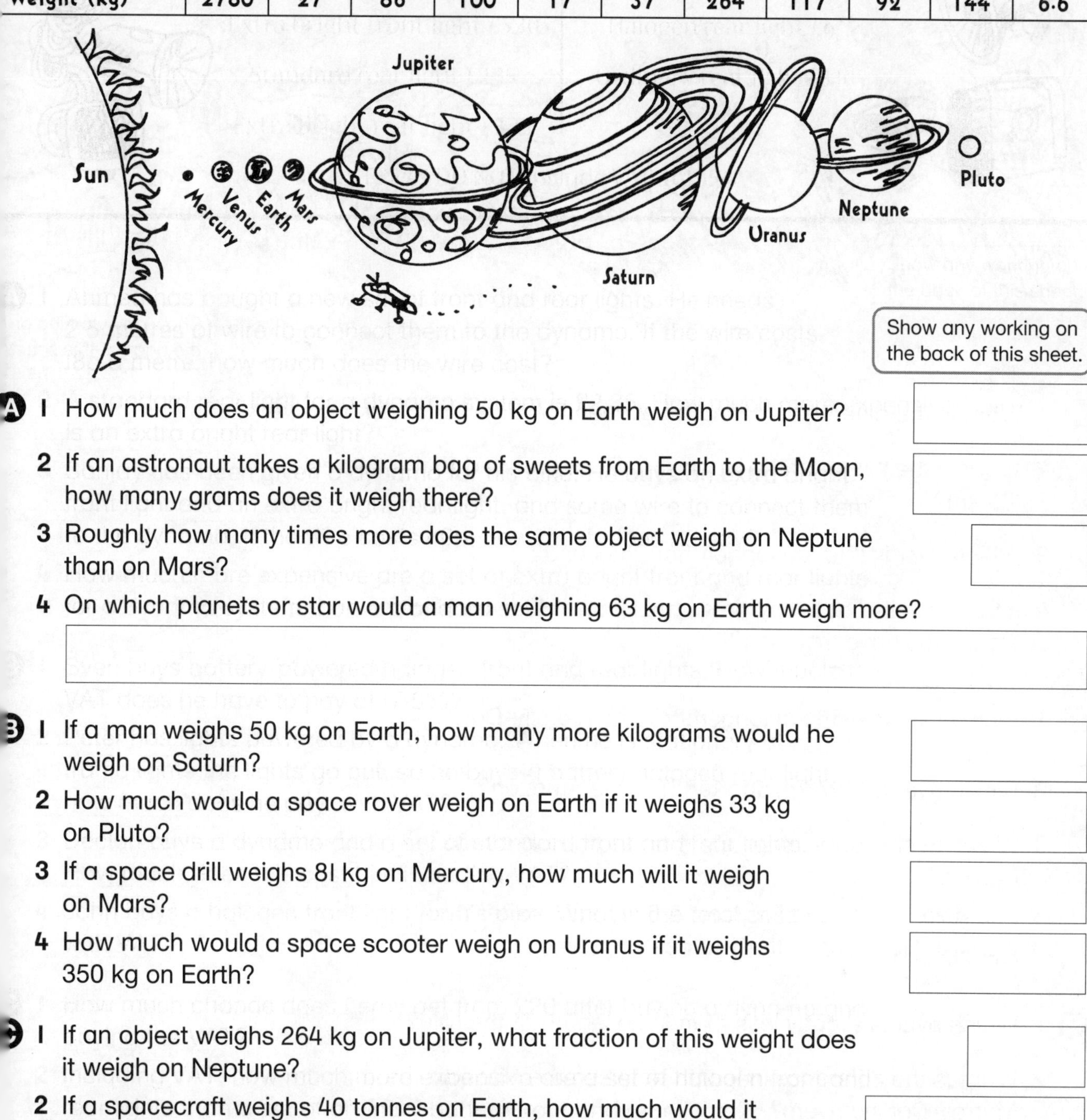

Show any working on the back of this sheet.

A 1 How much does an object weighing 50 kg on Earth weigh on Jupiter?

2 If an astronaut takes a kilogram bag of sweets from Earth to the Moon, how many grams does it weigh there?

3 Roughly how many times more does the same object weigh on Neptune than on Mars?

4 On which planets or star would a man weighing 63 kg on Earth weigh more?

B 1 If a man weighs 50 kg on Earth, how many more kilograms would he weigh on Saturn?

2 How much would a space rover weigh on Earth if it weighs 33 kg on Pluto?

3 If a space drill weighs 81 kg on Mercury, how much will it weigh on Mars?

4 How much would a space scooter weigh on Uranus if it weighs 350 kg on Earth?

C 1 If an object weighs 264 kg on Jupiter, what fraction of this weight does it weigh on Neptune?

2 If a spacecraft weighs 40 tonnes on Earth, how much would it weigh on Saturn?

3 An object weighs 1·65 kg on Pluto. How much does it weigh on Earth?

4 On which planet would it feel as though you were on Earth carrying a backpack weighing 1·64 times as much as you do?

Problems involving measures
Geography: 14. Investigating rivers

Name ____________________

Date ____________________

Longest rivers in the world

Nile – 6695 km *Africa*
Amazon – 6486 km *South America*
Yangtze – 6300 km *China*
Mississippi – 5993 km *USA*
Huang He – 5464 km *China*
Ob'-Irtysh – 5410 km *Russia*
Zaire – 4529 km *Africa*
Lena – 4400 km *Russia*
Mekong – 4180 km *Asia*
Niger – 4114 km *Africa*
Parana – 3943 km *South America*
Murray-Darling – 3751 km *Australia*

Show any working on the back of this sheet.

A

1 What is the difference in length between the Niger and Mekong rivers?

2 What is the length of the Huang He River rounded to the nearest 100 km?

3 Which river is 1010 km longer than the Lena?

4 If you travelled half way down the Huang He river, how far would you have travelled?

B

1 Which river is 1659 km longer than the Murray-Darling?

2 Which river is 1957 km shorter than the Amazon?

3 Which river is approximately $1\frac{1}{2}$ times as long as the Parana?

4 The River Thames in England is 6357 km shorter than the Nile. How long is the Thames?

C

1 Which river is slightly less than $\frac{2}{3}$ the length of the Nile?

2 What is the difference in length between the Nile and the Murray-Darling rivers?

3 If you took 50 days to travel down the whole length of the River Lena in Russia, travelling the same distance each day, how far would you have travelled after 2 weeks?

4 How many days would a boat travelling at 15 km an hour take to travel the length of the Yangtze River?

Problems involving measures
Geography: 15. The mountain environment

Name ____________________

Date ____________________

Mountain ranges

Mountain range	Length	Location
Trans-Atlantic Mountains	3541 km	*Antarctica*
Andes	7242 km	*South America*
Brazilian East Coast Range	3058 km	*Brazil*
Tien Shan	2253 km	*China*
Rocky Mountains	6035 km	*North America*
Sumatra/Java Range	2897 km	*Asia*
Eastern Ghats	2092 km	*India*
Great Dividing Range	3621 km	*Australia*
Himalayas	3862 km	*Asia*
Urals	2012 km	*Russia*

Show any working on the back of this sheet.

A

1 How much shorter are the Trans-Atlantic Mountains than the Great Dividing Range?

2 Which mountain range is 241 km longer than the Urals?

3 Which mountain range is almost three times longer than the Urals?

4 The highest mountain in the world is Mount Everest at 8846 m. The highest mountain in the UK is Ben Nevis at 1343 m. How much shorter is Ben Nevis than Mount Everest?

B

1 How much longer is the Great Dividing Range than the Brazilian East Coast Range?

2 Which mountain range is $\frac{1}{3}$ longer than the Sumatra/Java Range?

3 The Andes are twice as long as which mountain range?

4 Which mountain range is 321 km shorter than the Himalayas?

C

1 The Tien Shan are 1368 km shorter than which mountain range?

2 The longest mountain range on land is the Andes. The longest undersea mountain range is 11 265 km long. How much longer is it than the Andes?

3 Which mountain range is just under $\frac{4}{5}$ the length of the Himalayas?

4 Which two mountain ranges together are 80 km shorter than the Andes?

Problems involving measures
Geography: 15. The mountain environment

Name ____________________

Date ____________________

Mountain weather

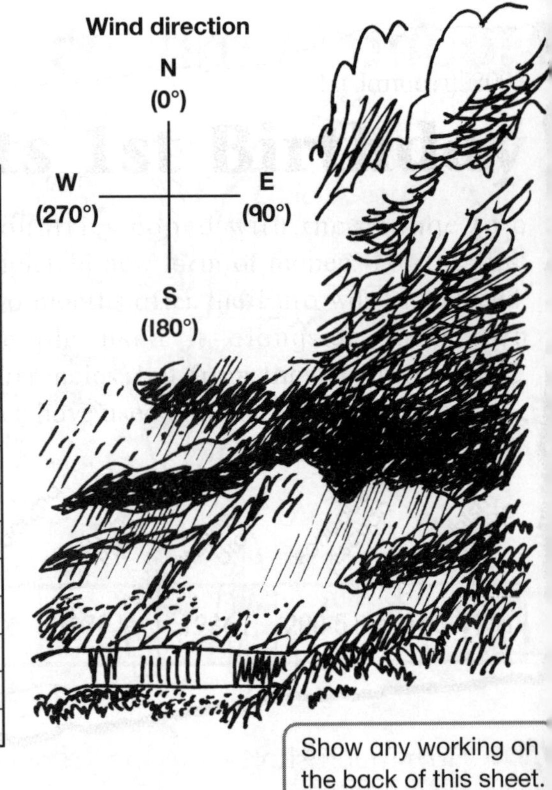

At 1085 metres, Snowdon is the highest mountain in Wales.

Month	Average temperature (°C)	Maximum wind speed (miles per hour)	Average wind direction (°)	Total Rainfall (mm)
January	−1·5	51·90	74	118
February	−4·4	29·37	53	137·8
March	−1·7	11·72	45	86·4
April	0·6	25·24	42	159·8
May	5·9	27·08	120	126·9
June	6·7	34·63	139	174·9
July	10	34·90	78	163·5
August	9·6	34·94	90	160·3
September	7·1	44·26	143	92·6
October	7·1	51·71	135	208·2
November	2·6	41·17	143	86
December	−0·2	34·36	50	69·6

Show any working on the back of this sheet.

A
1 What is the difference in temperature between the hottest and the coldest month?

2 In which month did the wind blow mainly from the East?

3 How much more rain fell in April than in March?

4 What is the difference between the fastest and slowest maximum wind speeds?

B
1 What is the difference in rainfall between the driest and the wettest months?

2 How much less rain fell in April than in October?

3 Which two consecutive months saw a temperature difference of 2·3°C?

4 From which direction did the wind blow most often in March?

C
1 What was the total amount of rainfall on Snowdon in the year?

2 What was the average temperature for the year on Snowdon, rounded to one decimal place?

3 In which month did the wind blow mainly from the south-east?

4 How much rain fell each month on Snowdon, averaged over the year?

Activity **26**

Problems involving measures

Geography: 16. What's in the news?

Name ______________________

Date ______________________

Who's best at recycling?

Who's best at recycling in Europe?

The table opposite shows, on average, how many kilograms of household waste each person produces a year in 10 European countries. The table also shows what percent of this waste is recycled, burnt or buried.

	Austria	Denmark	Finland	France	Germany	Ireland	Italy	Netherlands	Switzerland	UK
Kilograms of household waste	310	500	180	410	380	290	400	470	430	460
% recycled	38	23	33	9	30	8	0	38	40	7
% burnt	14	55	2	32	18	0	6	27	46	10
% buried	48	22	65	59	52	92	94	35	14	83

Show any working on the back of this sheet.

A 1 How much more waste does each person in the Netherlands produce than in Austria?

2 More waste in buried than burnt in Austria. How many percent more?

3 Each person in the UK produces 460 kg of waste. 10% of this is burnt. How many kilograms is this?

4 Italy buries a larger percentage of waste than any other country. How many more percent is this than France?

B 1 How much waste does a family of 6 in the UK produce?

2 How many kilograms of household waste are recycled for each person in Germany?

3 Finland buries 65% of its waste. How much is this per person?

4 People in the UK produce 460 kg of waste each and burn 10%. People in Austria produce 310 kg and burn 14%. Who burns less? How much less?

C 1 People in the Netherlands produce 470 kg of waste each. How many kilograms of this is recycled or burnt?

2 What is the difference in kilograms between the amount of waste that is burnt and the amount of waste that is buried for each person in Italy?

3 Which country burns on average 275 kg of waste per person?

4 Apart from Italy, which country recycles the least percent of waste per person? How many kilograms is this?

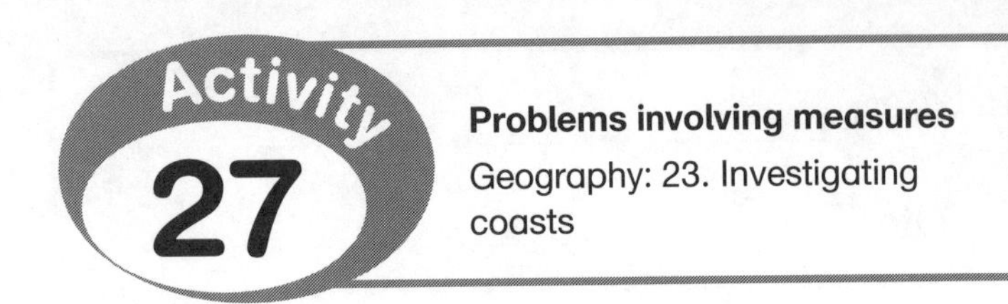

Problems involving measures

Geography: 23. Investigating coasts

Name ______________________

Date ______________________

Where land meets sea

Show any working on the back of this sheet

A

1. The difference between high tide and low tide in England is 4·5 m on average. In Bristol this difference is 12 m. How much greater is the difference in Bristol than the average?
2. Earthquakes or landslides can cause giant waves. The highest wave ever recorded was 524 m high. The tallest building in the world is 452 m high. How much higher was the wave?
3. The spinning of the Earth and the pull of the moon cause tides. There are 2 high tides approximately every 24 hr and 50 min. How much time is there between each high tide?
4. In Cardiff, the sea is 11·4 m high at high tide and 1·8 m high at low tide. What is the difference in height between high and low tide?

B

1. At Mont St Michel in France, the tide comes in so fast that people on the beach can find themselves $\frac{1}{2}$ km from land within 15 minutes. At this rate, how far does the water travel in 1 hour?
2. At Mont St Michel in France, the sea rises 9 metres in about 6 hours between high tide and low tide. How far does it rise each hour?
3. A wave breaks when the depth of the sea is $\frac{2}{3}$ the height of the wave. If a wave is 1·8 m high, how deep is the sea when it breaks?
4. At Plymouth, high tide is at 05:55. If the next low tide is 6 hr 12 min later, at what time is the next low tide?

C

1. If a wave that breaks on a beach was formed 24 hours ago by a storm at sea 720 km away, how far has this wave travelled each hour?
2. On Christmas Day in Dover, high tide was at 14:37. The next high tide was at 03:08 the next day. How long was there between the two high tides?
3. At Cardiff the sea is 11·3 m high at high tide and 1·8 m high at low tide. How high is the sea half way between high tide and low tide?
4. On Christmas Eve in Aberdeen low tide was at 09:54. The next low tide was 12 hr 41 min later. At what time was it?

Problems involving measures
Geography: 23. Investigating coasts

Name ______________________

Date ______________________

How long are their coastlines?

Country	Length of coastline (km)
Australia	25 760
Canada	243 791
China	14 500
Greece	13 676
Greenland	44 086
Indonesia	54 716
Japan	29 761
New Zealand	15 134
Norway	21 925
Philippines	36 288
Russia	37 201
USA	19 925

Show any working on the back of this sheet.

A 1 The coastline of Japan is longer than that of Australia. How much longer?

2 Which country has a coastline roughly 40 000 km longer than China's?

3 How much longer is the coastline of New Zealand than that of China?

4 Which country has a coastline approximately 8 times longer than Japan's?

B 1 Russia's coastline is 37 201 km long. Which country has a coastline 22 067 km shorter?

2 Which country has a coastline about $\frac{2}{3}$ as long as Japan's?

3 The coast of Greenland is longer than that of the USA. How much longer?

4 Japan has a coastline of 29 761 km. The coastlines of two other countries, when added together, are 127 km shorter than this. Which two countries?

C 1 How much longer is the coastline of Canada than that of Norway?

2 Which country's coastline is 22 612 km longer than Greece's?

3 Japan's coastline is 29 761 km long. Which country has a coastline $1\frac{1}{4}$ times as long?

4 Which country has a coastline nearly $\frac{2}{5}$ as long as the Philippines?

Problems involving measures
Geography: 23. Investigating coasts

Name ______________________

Date ______________________

Falling cliffs

The north-east coastline of England has been eroding rapidly for centuries. The table below shows the rate at which the fastest eroding stretch of coastline has been lost to the sea. This coastline, about 60 km long, has been divided into 4 sections that show different rates of erosion.

Cliff retreat

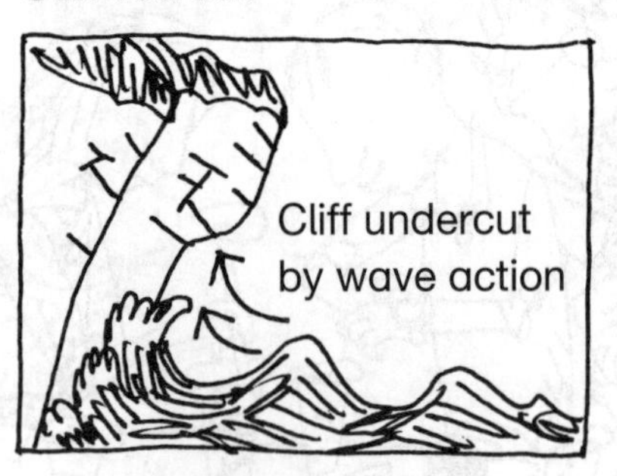

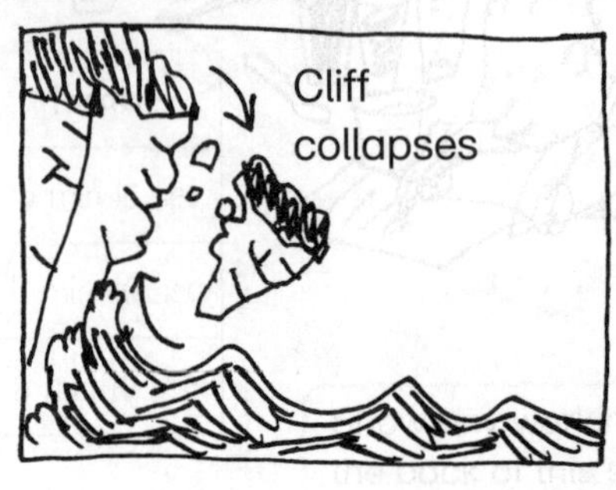

Section	Length of section (m)	Yearly cliff retreat (m)	Average cliff height (m)
1	8100	0·29	11·0
2	13 650	1·10	11·8
3	24 250	1·12	16·2
4	15 524	1·75	13·2

Show any working on the back of this sheet.

A
1. How much lower are the cliffs in section 2 than in section 4?
2. 1·75 m of cliff is lost each year in section 4. How much more is this than in section 3?
3. Section 3 is 24 250 m long. How many kilometres is this?
4. Section 4 is 15 524 m long. How much longer is it than section 1?

B
1. What is the difference in yearly cliff retreat between the section that erodes the fastest and the section that erodes the slowest?
2. What is the total length of all 4 sections, in kilometres and metres?
3. In section 3, the cliffs retreat 1·12 m each year. At this rate how far do they retreat in 50 years?
4. How much further do the cliffs in section 4 retreat in 20 years than those in section 2?

C
1. The area of land that is lost each year in section 2 is 13 650 m long by 1·1 m wide. What is the area, in square metres, that is lost?
2. What is the area of land, in square metres, that is lost in a century in section 1?
3. The area of land that is lost each year in section 4 is 27 167 m^2. The area lost in section 1 is only 2349 m^2. How much more land is lost each year in section 4?
4. What is the total area of land that is lost each year in all 4 sections together?

Problems involving measures
History: 16. How can we find out about the Indus Valley civilisation?

Name ______________________

Date ______________________

Weighing things in Harappa

Sets of cube-shaped weights have been found at Harappa.
The six weights below show some of the standard sizes excavated there.

A: 0·856 g B: 1·712 g C: 3·424 g D: 6·848 g E: 13·7 g F: 1·37 kg

Show any working on the back of this sheet.

A 1 If an ancient Harappan bought rice equal in weight to two Block F weights, how many kilograms of rice is this?

2 How many times heavier is Block F than Block E?

3 What is the difference in weight between Block B and Block D?

4 If an ancient Harappan bought silver weighing the same as six Block Es, how many grams of silver is this?

B 1 Block A weighs 0·856 g. How many times heavier is Block B?

2 Which two blocks together weigh 15·412 grams?

3 How many grams heavier is Block E than Block A?

4 If an ancient Harappan sold gold dust weighing the same as one Block A and one Block D, how many grams of gold is this?

C 1 What is the ratio of the weight of Block A to Block B to Block C to Block D?

2 If an ancient Harappan bought grain weighing five Block Es and seven block Fs, how many kilograms and grams is this?

3 Roughly how many times heavier is Block E than Block A?

4 What is the maximum weight that can be weighed using one each of the six weights above?

Activity 31

Problems involving 'real life' and measures

Science: 6A. Interdependence and adaptation

Name ______________________

Date ______________________

The Serengeti National Park

The Serengeti National Park in Africa covers an area of 1476 km² and is mainly grassland plains. It has the greatest concentration of plains animals of any place in Africa. It is considered to be the planet's greatest and most spectacular ecosystem.

Show any working on the back of this sheet.

A

1 In the Serengeti there are 500 000 Thompson's gazelle, 32 000 Grant's gazelle, 72 000 topi and 18 000 eland. How many is this altogether?

2 A lioness eats about 2700 kg of meat each year. A lion eats $\frac{1}{3}$ more than this. How much does a lion eat in a year?

3 A lioness eats about 2700 kg of meat each year. How much does a pride of 6 lionesses eat in a year?

4 When two or more lions hunt together they are successful 30% of the time. For every 50 times they hunt, how many times are they likely to catch their prey?

B

1 Lions eat 25 kg of meat at a time, but they don't eat every day. If a zebra weighs 275 kg, how many lions will it feed?

2 There are 1357 elephants in the Serengeti. An elephant eats 200 kg of vegetation each day. What is the total amount of vegetation eaten each day by the elephants in the park?

3 Wildebeest weigh about 225 kg each. If a lioness needs 2700 kg of meat each year, how many wildebeest must she eat?

4 There are 7500 hyenas in the Serengeti. They eat mainly dead animals, but they do hunt small or weak ones. If they hunt in packs of roughly 20 hyenas, how many packs is this?

C

1 There are 1·4 million wildebeest in the Serengeti. This is 56 times more than the number of buffalo. How many buffalo are there in the park?

2 The Serengeti National Park covers an area of 1476 km². How many square metres is this?

3 When a lion hunts alone it is successful in catching its prey 15% of the time. Out of every 20 animals it chases, how many will it catch?

4 There are 3000 lions in the Serengeti. If each lion eats approximately 3000 kg a year and wildebeest weigh about 225 kg each, how many wildebeest are eaten each year by the lions?

Activity 32

Problems involving 'real life' and measures

Science: 6A. Interdependence and adaptation

Name ______________________

Date ______________________

Meerkats stand tall

Meerkats live in the harsh environment of the Kalahari Desert in Africa. They live in groups, called mobs, of up to 40 animals and are probably the most co-operative mammals on earth.

Show any working on the back of this sheet.

A

1 Meerkats are 0·3 metres tall and have a tail 0·2 metres long that they use to balance themselves when they stand up. In centimetres, how long is a meerkat in total?

2 The ruling pair of meerkats in the mob produces 80% of the babies. If there are 5 baby meerkats in a mob, how many have been produced by the ruling pair of meerkats?

3 Only $\frac{1}{4}$ of baby meerkats live to become adults. Out of 36 babies how many will live to become adults?

4 All adult meerkats take turns to baby-sit while the other adults feed. If 2 adults baby-sit at a time for 2 hours, how many adults are needed for 12 hours?

B

1 Meerkats weigh about 0·9 kg. If their home is attacked, a mob can drive away a 12 kg jackal. Approximately how many times heavier is a jackal than a meerkat?

2 Meerkats weigh about 0·9 kg. If a meerkat does not eat for a day it loses 2% of its weight. How much weight does a meerkat lose in a day if it does not eat?

3 Meerkats eat insects, eggs and small reptiles. They hunt for food for 7 hours each day. What proportion of the day is spent hunting?

4 A mob of meerkats has a territory approximately $3\frac{1}{2}$ km by $3\frac{1}{2}$ km. How many square kilometres is this?

C

1 Meerkats live in mobs of around 40 animals. How many meerkats are there in 320 mobs?

2 Meerkats reach adult size by the time they are 18 months old. If they live for 12 years, for what fraction of their life are they full size?

3 A mob of meerkats has a territory approximately $3\frac{1}{2}$ km by $3\frac{1}{2}$ km. How many mobs will there be in an area of 50 km^2?

4 Meerkats have very good eyesight and can spot an eagle in the sky 1000 feet away. If 1 m equals 3·25 feet, how many metres is this to the nearest metre?

Activity 33

Problems involving 'real life' and measures

Science: 6C. More about dissolving

Name ________________

Date ________________

Extracting salt by evaporation

Sea water contains salt dissolved in it. In hot countries near the sea, this salt is extracted from the sea by pumping sea water into large ponds where the water evaporates off leaving the salt behind.

Show any working on the back of this sheet.

A

1 If an evaporation pond is 120 m long by 40 m wide, what is the area of the pond?

2 If the depth of the water in the evaporation pond has gone down by 35 cm after 6 months, how far will it have gone down after 18 months?

3 It takes 65 tonnes of sea water to produce 1 tonne of salt. How many tonnes of sea water do you need to produce 5 tonnes of salt?

4 If one evaporation pond produces $\frac{5}{8}$ of a tonne of salt, how many tonnes of salt do 16 ponds produce?

B

1 After 18 months in the evaporation pond, the sea water has reduced in volume by 90% due to evaporation. At this rate what percentage of the water has evaporated after a year?

2 When sea water 1 m deep evaporates completely, it leaves a layer of salt 15 mm deep. How many millimetres of salt is left behind when a depth of 0·6 m of sea water evaporates?

3 Every 1000 litres of sea water contains 35 kg of salt. The Dead Sea in Israel is about 11 times saltier than this. How many kilograms of salt would you get from 1000 litres of Dead Sea water?

4 1000 litres of fresh water weighs 1000 kg. 1000 litres of sea water weighs 1035 kg. How much does 40 000 litres of sea water weigh?

C

1 1 tonne of salt is produced from 65 tonnes of sea water. How many tonnes of sea water do you need to produce 45 tonnes of salt?

2 Every 1000 litres of sea water contains 35 kg of salt. How many litres of sea water do you need to produce 100 kg of salt, to the nearest litre?

3 When the water evaporates completely from the evaporation ponds, 35 kg of salt is left on each square metre of the bottom of the pond. If the area of the pond is 4800 m², how many kilograms of salt are left?

4 Every 1000 litres of sea water contains 35 kg of salt. The Dead Sea in Israel is 10·7 times saltier than this. How many grams of salt would you get from one litre of Dead Sea water?

Problems involving 'real life' and measures
Science: 6D. Reversible and irreversible changes

Name ____________________

Date ____________________

Reversible and irreversible cooking

REVERSIBLE COOKING

Fruit jelly

80 cl strawberry jelly
105 g strawberries
1 apple
1 orange
1 pear

IRREVERSIBLE COOKING

Fruit cake

450 g currants
175 g sultanas
175 g raisins
50 g glacé cherries
50 g mixed peel
225 g flour
$\frac{1}{2}$ teaspoon salt
$\frac{1}{4}$ teaspoon nutmeg
$\frac{2}{3}$ teaspoon mixed spice
50 g almonds
225 g brown sugar
225 g butter
4 eggs

Show any working on the back of this sheet.

A 1 How many grams of flour, almonds, sugar and butter are needed to make the fruit cake?

2 It takes 25 minutes to melt the jelly over a bowl of hot water before mixing in the chopped fruit. It then takes 2 hours 30 minutes for it to solidify in the fridge. How many times longer does it take to solidify than to melt?

3 If the average weight of an egg is 70 grams, how many kilograms do 4 eggs weigh?

4 When the fruit has been added to the melted jelly, the volume of the mixture is 1·15 litres. If the jelly mould holds a maximum of $1\frac{1}{4}$ litres, how many more millilitres of mixture could it hold?

B 1 How many grams of currants, sultanas, raisins, cherries and mixed peel are there altogether in the fruit cake?

2 If it takes 40 minutes to mix the cake and $4\frac{3}{4}$ hours to bake it, how long does it take altogether to make the cake?

3 80 cl of jelly is melted and chopped fruit is added. The volume of the mixture is now 1·15 litres. How much fruit has been added, in litres?

4 What is the ratio of currants to raisins to cherries in the fruit cake?

C 1 The volume of the jelly is 1·15 litres. If $\frac{3}{5}$ is eaten, how much is left?

2 What is the ratio of salt to nutmeg to mixed spice in the fruit cake?

3 Altogether, how many teaspoons of salt, nutmeg and mixed spice go into the fruit cake?

4 If eggs weigh 70 g each and the salt, nutmeg and mixed spice weigh 20 g altogether, what is the total weight of the cake before it is cooked?

Problems involving 'real life' and measures

Science: 6D. Reversible and irreversible changes

Name ______________________

Date ______________________

Reversible processes, reusable resources

Water and paper are two items of household consumption that are regularly recycled. Dirty water is treated by filtration and purification and then reused. After use, paper is transformed back into pulp, sterilised and made again into paper. The dirtying of water and the turning of paper into pulp are both reversible processes. The table below shows the percentage of paper and water recycled by ten different countries.

	Austria	Canada	France	Germany	Greece	Mexico	Portugal	Spain	Switzerland	UK
% paper recycled	65	33	38	67	19	2	37	52	67	37
% water recycled	74·7	78	77	87·2	56·2	21·8	20·7	48·3	94	86

Show any working on the back of this sheet.

A

1 What is the difference between the percentage of water recycled in Mexico and Switzerland?

2 How much more paper does Austria recycle than France, as a percentage?

3 Which country recycles 18% more paper than Greece?

4 Which countries recycle more than half of the paper they use?

B

1 Which country recycles 65·3% more water than Portugal?

2 Most people in Austria use about 200 kg of paper a year. If 65% of this is recycled, how many kilograms are recycled for each person in a year?

3 Which country recycles four times as much water as Mexico?

4 As a percentage, how much less water does Spain recycle than Greece?

C

1 Each person in Canada uses 497 litres of water a day. How many litres are recycled each day per person to the nearest litre?

2 Most people in Mexico use about 36 kg of paper a year. If 2% of this is recycled, how many grams are recycled per person per year?

3 People in both Germany and the UK use 191 kg of paper each a year. How many more kilograms per person are recycled in Germany than in the UK each year?

4 Each person in Switzerland uses 209 kg of paper a year, of which 67% is recycled. Each person in Greece uses 88 kg per year, of which only 19% is recycled. Which country wastes more kilograms of paper per person per year? How many kilograms more?

Problems involving 'real life', money and measures
Science: 6F. How we see things

Name ______________________

Date ______________________

Projectors

Overhead projectors and cinema projectors have a very bright light that shines through a piece of film. The dark parts of the film cut out the light and create a shadow on the screen. The transparent parts of the film let the light through onto the screen.

Show any working on the back of this sheet.

A

1. A film club meets twice a month. Each time it costs them £187 to hire the cinema and £135 to hire the film. How much does it cost them each month?
2. Mr. Lee draws a picture and projects it onto a screen using an overhead projector. His drawing is 15 cm long. When it appears on the screen it is 5 times bigger. How long is the drawing on the screen?
3. The local cinema used to have one screen and seated 350 people. It has now been converted into three smaller cinemas that seat 56 people, 73 people and 172 people. How many fewer people does it seat now?
4. Mr. Lee projects a picture of an animal onto a screen using an overhead projector. The animal on the screen is 93 cm. If the drawing is 14 cm high, how many centimetres bigger is the image?

B

1. 6L are using an overhead projector to trace a silhouette of their heads. Lisa's head is 224 mm. Her silhouette is 316 mm. How many millimetres bigger is the silhouette?
2. A local cinema holds 250 people and charges £5.50 a ticket. If it costs the cinema £246 to hire a film, what is the minimum number of tickets the cinema needs to sell to pay for the film?
3. The screen in 6L's classroom is 1·5 m by 2 m. The screen in the cinema is 11 m by 6 m. How much larger is the area of the cinema screen?
4. If an actor is 3·2 m high on a cinema screen but only 1·73 m in real life, how many centimetres taller is he on the screen?

C

1. If Mr. Lee walks between the screen and the projector near to the screen, the shadow from his head is 38 cm high. If he walks between them near to the projector, his head is 1 m 14 cm high. How many times bigger is this?
2. In the cinema, the ratio of the width of the picture to its height is 1·85 : 1. If the picture is 6 m high, how wide is it?
3. A cinema seats 450 and charges £7 for adults and £4 for children. Last weekend it was sold out for every screening. If the film was shown 6 times and $\frac{2}{3}$ of the audience were children, how much money did it take last weekend?
4. Most films are made on 35 mm wide film. When the picture reaches the screen it can be 10 m wide. How many times bigger is the picture than the film, rounded to the nearest whole number?

Activity 37

Problems involving 'real life', money and measure

Geography: 15. The mountain environment

Name ____________________

Date ____________________

The Alps

The Alps are the highest and largest mountain range in Europe.

Show any working on the back of this sheet.

A 1 The Alps are 1000 km long and cover an area of 240 000 km^2. How wide are the Alps?

2 The highest mountain in the Alps is Mont Blanc at 4807 m. If most mountains in the Alps are about 3500 m high, how much higher than this is Mont Blanc?

3 100 million people visited the Alps in 2002. How many people was this each week to the nearest million?

4 100 million people visited the Alps in 2002. 3 million of them went mountain biking. What percentage is this?

B 1 At 8846 m, Mount Everest is the highest mountain in the world. At 4807 m, Mont Blanc is the highest mountain in Europe. What is the difference in height?

2 100 million tourists visited the Alps in 2002. 0·8% of these took part in extreme water sports such as canyoning and rafting. How many tourists did this in 2002?

3 The Alps cover an area of 240 000 km^2. Protected areas cover 11% of this. How much land is protected?

4 Plants and animals only flourish in the Alps where humans are totally excluded. They are only excluded from 2400 km^2 of the total area of 240 000 km^2. What percentage is this?

C 1 1·5 million people visited Gran Paradiso Park in the Italian Alps. 700 000 people visited another alpine park in Italy, and 1 million people visited alpine parks in Germany and France. What percentage of the 100 million tourists visited these four parks in 2002?

2 12 million walkers stayed in 1600 high altitude mountain huts in 2002. On average, how many people stayed in each hut in the year?

3 Tourism in the whole world is worth £288 billion each year. 25% of this comes from tourism in the Alps. How much money is tourism in the Alps worth?

4 100 million tourists visited the Alps in 2002. The number of tourists is increasing by 4% each year. At this rate, how many people visit the Alps in 2004?

Problems involving 'real life', money and measures

History: 12. How did life change in our locality in Victorian times?

Name ______________________

Date ______________________

How trains changed the Victorians

3ritain's rail network was built very quickly. In 836 there were only 400 miles of track. In 1840 here were 1500 miles, in 1850, 5000 miles and y 1870, 15 500 miles. The railways were elatively cheap and everyone, rich or poor, ould afford to travel.

THE MIDLAND RAILWAY COMPANY WILL RUN
TWO TRAINS DAILY

For the Great Exhibition

1st Class: 75p return

2nd Class: 50p return

3rd Class: 25p return

Children aged between 3 and 12 years: half price
(Prices include entry to the Exhibition.)

Show any working on the back of this sheet.

A

1 The amount of railway track in Britain increased from 1500 miles in 1840 to 15 500 miles in 1870. How many miles more was this?

2 How much did it cost a family of 2 adults and 3 children, aged 6, 8 and 10, to travel from York to London second class and visit the Exhibition?

3 The train fare from London to Brighton in 1843 was 18·5p. How much did it cost for 4 people?

4 In Victorian times, a city labourer earned £1 a week. What fraction of his weekly wage would he spend if he bought a 3rd class ticket from York to London to see the Great Exhibition?

B

1 The first public railway in Britain opened in 1825. 38 years later the world's first Underground train line opened in London. Which year was this?

2 By 1880, the journey from London to Edinburgh took 10 hours by train. It used to take 69 hours by horse and coach. How much quicker was the journey by train, in days and hours?

3 A farm labourer earned 70p a week in Victorian times. How many weeks would he need to work to take himself, his wife and 4 children under 12 from York to London 3rd class to see the Exhibition?

4 In 1850, 38 million tonnes of goods were carried by rail. By 1900 it was 419·8 million tonnes. By how many tonnes did it increase during this period?

C

1 In 1842, 24·7 million passengers travelled by rail. By 1900 this had increased to 1114·6 million. How many more passengers was this?

2 In 1887, a yearly ticket from Windsor to Paddington cost £18. If a man travelled to work, 5 days a week, 50 weeks a year, how much did this cost him for each day of travelling?

3 The population of Britain in 1900 was about 41 million. If 1114·6 million train journeys were made that year, what is the average number of journeys that each person made, rounded to the nearest journey?

4 First class passengers travelling by train to the Exhibition could take 112 lb of luggage with them. If 2·2 lb = 1 kg, approximately how many kilograms is this?

Problems involving 'real life', money and measures

History: 19. What were the effects of Tudor exploration?

Name ______________________

Date ______________________

Tudor sailors

Remember:
1 gallon = 4·5 litres
2·2 lb = 1 kg

Wage	50p a month
Biscuit	1 lb a day
Beer	1 gallon a day
Meat	4 lb a week
Fish	3 lb a week

Show any working on the back of this sheet.

A 1 How many litres of beer did each sailor get a week?

2 In a 4 week month, how many more pounds of biscuit did a sailor get than meat?

3 What was the ratio of fish to meat in a sailor's diet?

4 How much was a sailor paid each year?

B 1 Sir Francis Drake's ship, the Revenge, had 133 sailors. How many pounds of biscuit altogether did they eat in a week?

2 What was the monthly wage bill for all 133 sailors on the Revenge?

3 How many litres of beer did the 133 sailors drink each day?

4 There were 133 sailors on the Revenge. How many pounds of meat did they eat each day?

C 1 When Sir Francis Drake started his voyage around the world in his ship the Pelican, he had 164 sailors. How many pounds of meat did he have to take to last them for 4 weeks?

2 If Sir Francis Drake took 6000 gallons of beer, how many days would this last his crew of 164 sailors, to the nearest whole day?

3 Sir Francis Drake returned from his world voyage with 80 sailors. They had been away for 34 months. How much did he have to pay these sailors altogether?

4 How many kilograms of fish did Sir Francis Drake need to take with him for his crew of 164 sailors to last them for 11 weeks?

Problems involving 'real life', money and measures

History: 19. What were the effects of Tudor exploration?

Name ______________________

Date ______________________

A Tudor expedition

Expedition log
5 September 1589
Weight of entire fleet:
16 180 tonnes
Number of sailors paid up to this day: 1161
Wages paid up to this day: £2832.84

	Number of ships	Number of sailors in total
500 tonnes or more	2	400
400-499 tonnes	2	360
300-399 tonnes	5	410
200-299 tonnes	25	1038
100-199 tonnes	45	1141
Less than 100 tonnes	23	373

Show any working on the back of this sheet.

A

1 What was the total number of ships on the expedition?

2 How many more sailors were on ships of 300–399 tonnes than on ships of less than 100 tonnes?

3 How many sailors were on each of the ships weighing 400–499 tonnes if they each had the same number of sailors?

4 How many sailors were on ships of 300 tonnes or more?

B

1 There were fewer sailors on ships between 200–299 tonnes than on ships of less than 200 tonnes. How many fewer?

2 What was the total number of sailors on the expedition?

3 On average, how many sailors were on each of the ships weighing 300–399 tonnes?

4 1161 sailors had already been paid by 5th September 1589. How many sailors on the expedition had not yet been paid?

C

1 On average, how many sailors were there on each of the ships weighing 200–299 tonnes, to the nearest sailor?

2 1161 sailors were paid a total of £2832.84. How much was each sailor paid, on average?

3 If the weight of the entire fleet was 16 180 tonnes, roughly what was the average weight of each ship?

4 £2832.84 had already been spent on wages. If £34 776.16 more was spent on the expedition, how much did it cost in total?

Answers

Activity 1
Deadly microbes

A
1. 50 000
2. 11·5 million
3. 43%
4. 5 million

B
1. 68 million
2. $\frac{1}{65}$
3. 15 million
4. 10%

C
1. $\frac{1}{16}$
2. $\frac{1}{86}$
3. 250 000
4. 647 million

Activity 2
The force of air

A
1. 3 : 1
2. 2950 m
3. $\frac{2}{9}$
4. 336

B
1. 8500
2. 1937
3. 614 years
4. 4256

C
1. 53 min
2. $\frac{1}{25}$ or $\frac{1}{24}$
3. 3 min
4. 9 days, 18 hr

Activity 3
Communicating with the world

A
1. 545
2. 260
3. 1340
4. Belgium and UK

B
1. 247
2. 77·4%
3. $\frac{1}{8}$
4. 2250

C
1. 831
2. Australia
3. 72
4. 3 : 11

Activity 4
How they lived

A
1. 19·6%
2. 62·6%
3. 35·2%
4. 1 or 2 rooms/1%

B
1. 53 100
2. 83 159
3. 14 940
4. 248 826

C
1. 152 400 or 151 638 rounded
2. 32 205
3. 2950
4. 231 865

Activity 5
Jobs in Victorian times

A
1. 129
2. 330
3. 1740
4. 9517

B
1. 2957
2. 522
3. Men in commerce
4. 72·19%

C
1. 270
2. 1928
3. 12 : 1
4. 11·01%

Activity 6
Famous Greeks

A
1. 75 years
2. 570 BC
3. 70 years
4. 336 BC

B
1. 32 years old
2. 30
3. 460 BC
4. 347 BC

C
1. 34 years old
2. $\frac{1}{7}$
3. 46 years old
4. 27·5%

Activity 7
Democracy

A
1. 541
2. 247
3. 533
4. 6

B
1. 22 weeks
2. £55 116
3. 157
4. 330

C
1. 5580 hours
2. 42%
3. 1832 AD
4. 376

Activity 8
The Modern Olympics

A
1. 103
2. $\frac{6}{7}$
3. 25%
4. 30

B
1. 260
2. 163
3. 4 : 7 : 10
4. 1992 or Barcelona

C
1. $\frac{1}{52}$
2. USA
3. China 1996
4. 60

Activity 9
The Aztecs in the Valley of Mexico

A
1. 27
2. 22
3. 277
4. 745 000

B
1. 398
2. 728
3. 633
4. Hamlets

C
1. 1238
2. Regional centre
3. Religious centre
4. Small village

Activity 10
Nelson Mandela and the struggle against apartheid

A 1 75 years old
  2 £420
  3 28 years
  4 74

B 1 52 months
  2 256
  3 4·56 million
  4 19·44 million

C 1 4 years, 2 months and 29 days
  2 15
  3 110
  4 27·3%

Activity 11
Friendly microbes

A 1 13p
  2 Brie
  3 £2.35
  4 £3.12

B 1 £10.80
  2 £7.02
  3 £1.80
  4 27p

C 1 £7.20
  2 2 : 3
  3 £12.60
  4 500 g

Activity 12
Different mirrors

A 1 £24.72
  2 £238
  3 £331.40
  4 £282

B 1 £460.58
  2 35p
  3 £21.12
  4 £11.67

C 1 £1388
  2 £19.20
  3 £2808
  4 £1097.25

Activity 13
Wires and bulbs

A 1 £3.10
  2 4·8p
  3 £6.45
  4 80p

B 1 £8.68
  2 16·8p
  3 5 metres
  4 £98.90

C 1 £5.84
  2 88·48p
  3 £100.48
  4 312·5 hours

Activity 14
Lights for your bike

A 1 45p
  2 99p
  3 £9.04
  4 £2.13

B 1 £3.50
  2 £7.05
  3 £25.31
  4 £16.45

C 1 £1.20
  2 £13.85
  3 £2
  4 Halogen/6p

Activity 15
River travel in Sarawak, Borneo

A 1 92p
  2 £11
  3 £2.32
  4 £2.55

B 1 £240.92
  2 £5.95
  3 £26.68
  4 £117.56

C 1 25·5 Ringits
  2 £100
  3 £979
  4 £3.24

Activity 16
Recreation on the Thames

A 1 £52
  2 £117
  3 £1488
  4 £39

B 1 £138
  2 £20.20
  3 £50
  4 £1133

C 1 £21.75
  2 £5.25
  3 £882
  4 £7875

Activity 17
Spending the Euro

A 1 1·58 I£
  2 2 €
  3 59·5 Fmk
  4 5 €

B 1 123·84 Sh
  2 100 €
  3 8020 Esc
  4 20·17 BFr

C 1 2·94 €
  2 55·76 FFr
  3 5 €
  4 2329·6 Pta

Activity 18 Travelling the world

A 1 £816
2 £28
3 £465
4 New York

B 1 Jo'burg
2 £308
3 Los Angeles
4 £2352

C 1 £1600
2 £1337
3 £1895
4 £9011.70

Activity 19 Spending the £ since 1950

A 1 15%
2 11·3%
3 £135
4 £243.30

B 1 £850.90
2 £47.94
3 £81
4 Travel and communication

C 1 £1711.90
2 £14.52
3 £2376.52
4 £284.07

Activity 20 How the government spends its money

A 1 Education
2 £40 601 million
3 Health
4 £24·6 million

B 1 Benefit payments
2 £46 659 million
3 1970
4 Education

C 1 Health
2 Benefit payments
3 £147 153·3 million
4 Education/ 1990 and 2000

Activity 21 Dissolving different foodstuffs

A 1 Sugar
2 Instant coffee
3 490 seconds
4 Golden syrup at 40°C

B 1 Golden syrup
2 Treacle at 40°C
3 Sugar
4 890 seconds

C 1 Golden syrup at 0°C
2 Golden syrup at 20°C
3 Golden syrup at 40°C
4 10 : 7

Activity 22 Weight in space

A 1 132 kg
2 170 grams
3 4
4 Sun, Jupiter, Saturn, Neptune

B 1 8·5 kg
2 500 kg
3 111 kg
4 322 kg

C 1 $\frac{6}{11}$
2 46·8 tonnes or 46 800 kg
3 25 kg
4 Jupiter

Activity 23 Longest rivers in the world

A 1 66 km
2 5500 km
3 Ob'-Irtysh
4 2732 km

B 1 Ob'-Irtysh
2 Zaire
3 Mississippi
4 338 km

C 1 Lena
2 2944 km
3 1232 km
4 $17\frac{1}{2}$ days or 17 days 12 hours

Activity 24 Mountain ranges

A 1 80 km
2 Tien Shan
3 Rocky Mountains
4 7503 m

B 1 563 km
2 Himalayas
3 Great Dividing Range
4 Trans-Atlantic Mountains

C 1 Great Dividing Range
2 4023 km
3 Brazilian East Coast Range
4 Great Dividing Range and Trans-Atlantic Mountains

Activity 25 Mountain weather

A 1 14·4° C
2 August
3 73·4 mm
4 40·18 miles per hour

B 1 138·6 mm
2 48·4 mm
3 March and April
4 north-east

C 1 1584 mm
2 3·5° C
3 October
4 132 mm

Activity 26
Who's best at recycling?

A 1 160 kg
2 34%
3 46 kg
4 35%

B 1 2760 kg
2 114 kg
3 117 kg
4 Austria/2·6 kg

C 1 305·5 kg or 305 kg 500 g
2 352 kg
3 Denmark
4 UK/32·2 kg or 32 kg 200 g

Activity 27
Where land meets sea

A 1 7·5 m
2 72 m
3 12 hr 25 min
4 9·6 m

B 1 2 km
2 1·5 m
3 1·2 m
4 12:07 pm

C 1 30 km an hour
2 12 hr 31 min
3 6·55 m
4 22:35

Activity 28
How long are their coastlines?

A 1 4001 km
2 Indonesia
3 634 km
4 Canada

B 1 New Zealand
2 USA
3 24 161 km
4 New Zealand and China

C 1 221 866 km
2 Philippines
3 Russia
4 China

Activity 29
Falling cliffs

A 1 1·4 m
2 0·63 m
3 24·25 kilometres
4 7424 m or 7 km 424 m or 7·424 km

B 1 1·46 m
2 61 km 524 m
3 56 m
4 13 m

C 1 15 015 m^2
2 234 900 m^2
3 24 818 m^2
4 71 691 m^2

Activity 30
Weighing things in Harappa

A 1 2·74 kg
2 100
3 5·136 g
4 82·2 g

B 1 Twice
2 B and E
3 12·844 g
4 7·704 g

C 1 1 : 2 : 4 : 8
2 9 kg 658·5 g
3 16
4 1 kg 396·54 g

Activity 31
The Serengeti National Park

A 1 622 000
2 3600 kg
3 16 200 kg
4 15

B 1 11
2 271 400 kg
3 12
4 375

C 1 25 000
2 1476 million m^2
3 3
4 40 000

Activity 32
Meerkats stand tall

A 1 50 centimetres
2 4
3 9
4 12

B 1 13
2 18 g
3 7 out of 24 or $\frac{7}{24}$
4 12·25 km^2

C 1 12 800
2 $\frac{7}{8}$
3 4
4 308 m

Activity 33
Extracting salt by evaporation

A 1 4800 m^2
2 105 cm
3 325 tonnes
4 10 tonnes

B 1 60%
2 9 mm
3 385 kilograms
4 41 400 kg

C 1 2925 tonnes
2 2857 litres
3 168 000 kilograms
4 374·5 grams

Activity 34
Reversible and irreversible cooking

A 1 725 g
2 6
3 0·28 kilograms
4 100 millilitres

B 1 900 grams
2 5 hr 25 min
3 0·35 litres
4 18 : 7 : 2

C 1 0·46 litres or 460 ml
2 6 : 3 : 8
3 $1\frac{5}{12}$
4 1·925 kg or 1925 g

Activity 35
Reversible processes, reusable resources

A 1 72·2%
2 27%
3 Portugal
4 Austria, Germany, Spain, Switzerland

B 1 UK
2 130 kilograms
3 Germany
4 7·9%

C 1 388 litres
2 720 grams
3 57·3 kg
4 Greece/2·31 kg

Activity 36
Projectors

A 1 £644
2 75 cm
3 49
4 79 centimetres

B 1 92 millimetres
2 45
3 63 m^2 or 22 times
4 147 centimetres

C 1 3
2 11·1 m
3 £13 500
4 286

Activity 37
The Alps

A 1 240 km
2 1307 m
3 2 million
4 3%

B 1 4039 m
2 800 000
3 26 400 km^2
4 1%

C 1 3·2%
2 7500
3 £72 billion
4 108·16 million

Activity 38
How trains changed the Victorians

A 1 14 000 miles
2 £1.75
3 74p
4 $\frac{1}{4}$

B 1 1863
2 2 days and 11 hours
3 2 weeks
4 381·8 million

C 1 1089·9 million
2 7·2p
3 27
4 50·9 kg or 51 kg

Activity 39
Tudor sailors

A 1 31·5 litres
2 12 lb
3 3 : 4
4 £6

B 1 931 lb
2 £66.50
3 598·5 litres
4 76 lb

C 1 2624 lb
2 37 days
3 £1360
4 2460 kg

Activity 40
A Tudor expedition

A 1 102
2 37
3 180
4 1170

B 1 476
2 3722
3 82
4 2561

C 1 42
2 £2.44
3 Accept any answer in the range 157–162 tonnes
4 £37 609